Scope and Sequence
Level 1

UNIT	SOUNDS AND LETTERS	WORDS	ADDITIONAL WORDS	CVC WORDS
Hello	a b c d e f g h i j k l m n o p q r s t u v w x y z			
Unit 1	a, b, c	apple, bus, cat	ant, ball, coat	bus, cat
Unit 2	d, e, f	dog, elephant, fish	doll, egg, feet	dog
Unit 3	g, h, i	goat, hat, insect	girl, hands, ink	hat
Unit 4	j, k, l	juice, kite, leg	jump, key, lake	leg
Unit 5	m, n, o	moon, nest, octopus	mitten, nose, olive	mom
Unit 6	p, q, r	pencil, quilt, rabbit	pizza, queen, rain	red
Unit 7	s, t, u	sun, table, umbrella	seed, turtle, up	sun, cat
Unit 8	v, w, x	van, wheel, fox	violin, water, box	box, van, six
Unit 9	y, z	yogurt, zoo	yellow, zebra	bag, sun, ten, hop, hat, cat, fox, box, run

Hello

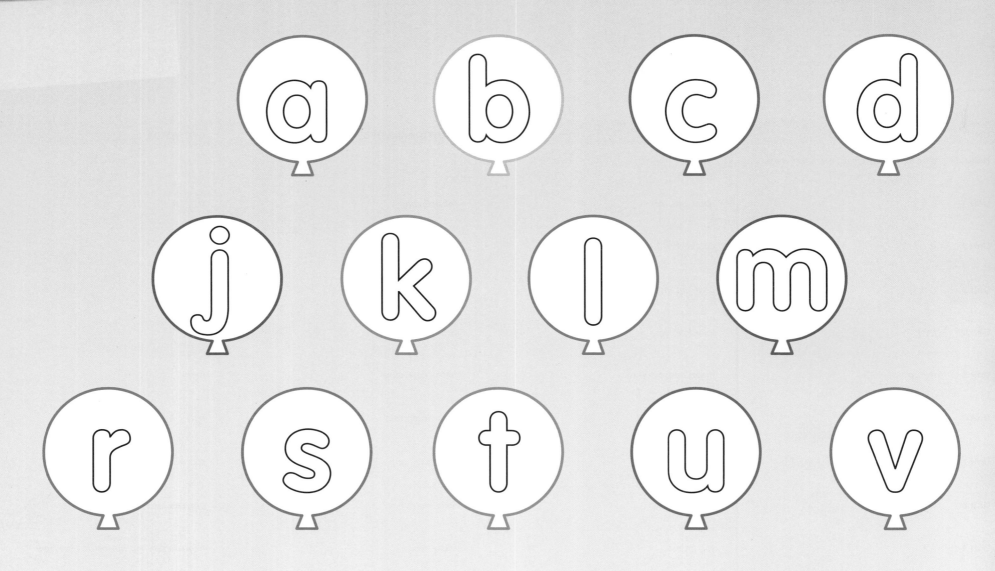

Hello
Alphabet

1 🔊 1.01 Listen and point.   2 🔊 1.02 Listen and chant.   3 Point and say.   4 Color.
Vocabulary: a–z

Unit 1

Unit 1
Letter a

1 🔊 1.03 Listen and chant. 2 🔊 1.04 Listen, say, and do. 3 Find the correct letters and color. 4 Trace or color the letter.
Vocabulary: apple

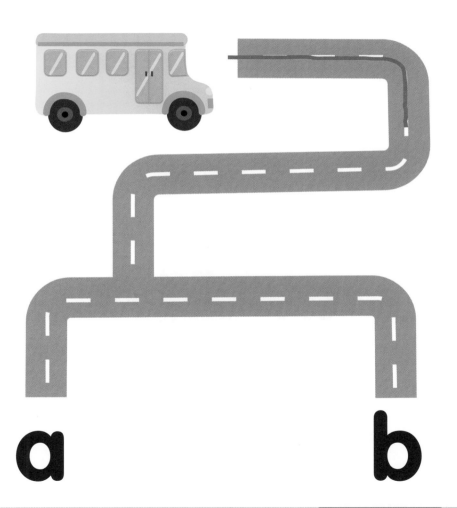

1 🔊 1.05 **Listen and chant.** 2 🔊 1.06 **Listen, say, and do.** 3 **Follow the maze and find the correct letter.** 4 **Trace or color the letter.**
Vocabulary: bus

Unit 1
Letter b

5

Unit 1
Letter c

1 🔊 1.07 **Listen and chant.**   2 🔊 1.08 **Listen, say, and do.**   3 **Find the correct letters and match.**   4 **Trace or color the letter.**
Vocabulary: cat

1 **Say the letter sounds.** 2 🔊 1.09 **Listen and say the words. Match.** 3 **Color the objects with the same color.** 4 **Trace the letters.**

Vocabulary: apple, bus, cat, ball, coat, **ant**

d

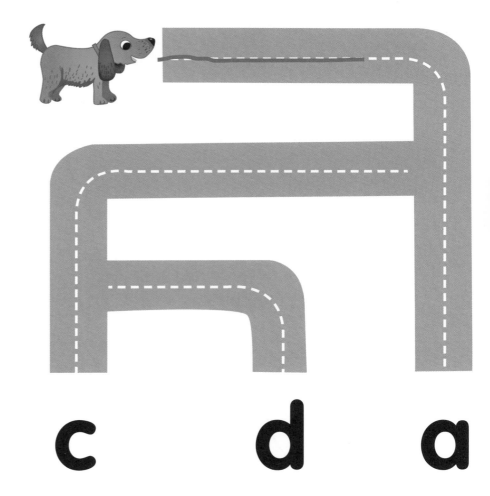

c   d   a

Unit 2
Letter d

1 📢 1.10 **Listen and chant.**   2 📢 1.11 **Listen, say, and do.**   3 **Follow the maze and find the correct letter.**   4 **Trace or color the letter.**
Vocabulary: dog

1 🔊 1.12 **Listen and chant.**   2 🔊 1.13 **Listen, say, and do.**   3 **Find the correct letter and color.**   4 **Trace or color the letter.**
Vocabulary: elephant

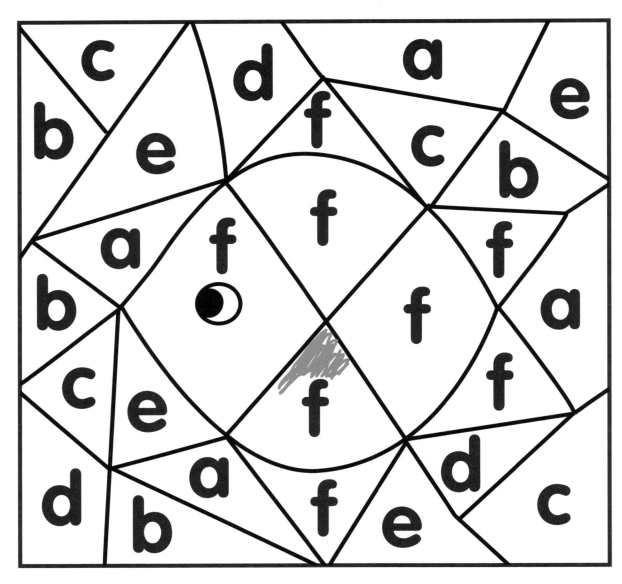

Unit 2
Letter f

1 🔊 1.14 Listen and chant.   2 🔊 1.15 Listen, say, and do.   3 Find the correct letters and color the picture.   4 Trace or color the letter.

Vocabulary: fish

Unit 2

Letters d, e, f

11

1 **Say the letter sounds.**   2 🔊 1.16 **Listen and say the words. Match.**   3 **Color the objects with the same color.**   4 **Trace the letters.**
Vocabulary: dog, elephant, fish, **feet**, doll, egg

Unit 3
Letter g

1 🔊1.17 **Listen and chant.**   2 🔊1.18 **Listen, say, and do.**   3 **Find the correct letters and color.**   4 **Trace or color the letter.**
Vocabulary: goat

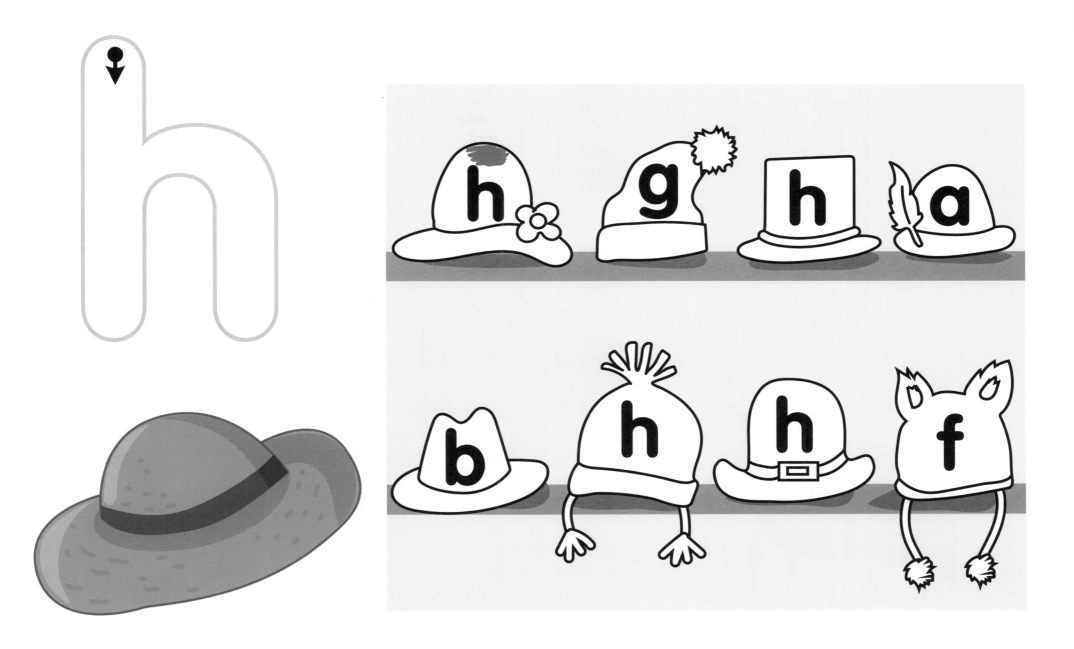

1 🔊 1.19 Listen and chant.   2 🔊 1.20 Listen, say, and do.   3 Find the correct letters and color.   4 Trace or color the letter.
Vocabulary: hat

Unit 3
Letter h

13

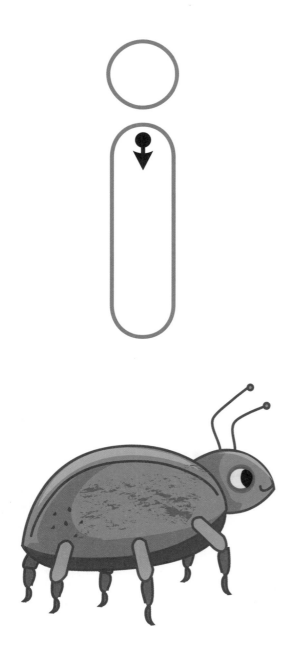

Unit 3
Letter i

1 🔊 1.21 Listen and chant.   2 🔊 1.22 Listen, say, and do.   3 Find and circle the letters.   4 Trace or color the letter.

Vocabulary: insect

1 **Say the letter sounds.**   2 🔊 **1.23** **Listen and say the words. Match.**   3 **Color the objects with the same color.**   4 **Trace the letters.**
Vocabulary: goat, hat, insect, hands, girl, **ink**

Unit 3
Letters g, h, i   **15**

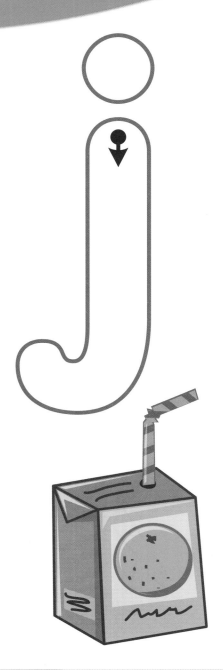

Unit 4
Letter j

Vocabulary: juice

1 🔊 1.24 **Listen and chant.**   2 🔊 1.25 **Listen, say, and do.**   3 **Find the correct letters and match.**   4 **Trace or color the letter.**

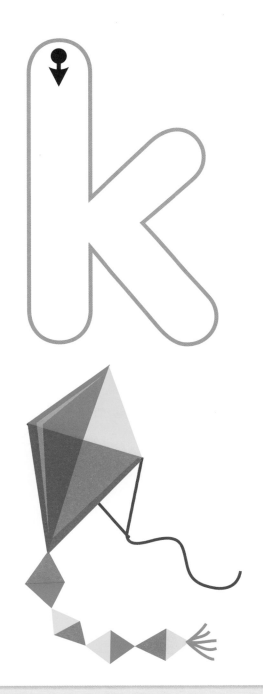

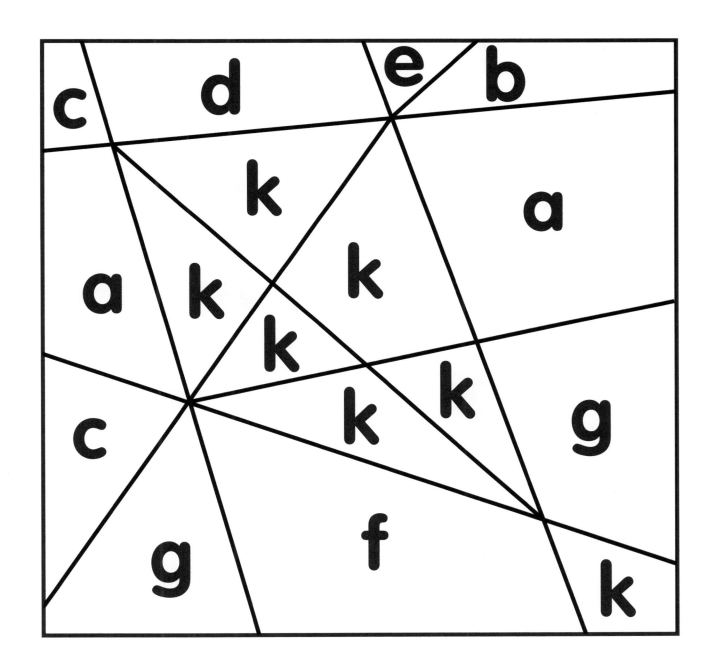

c d e b
k a
a k k
k
c k k g
g f
k

1 🔊 1.26 **Listen and chant.**   2 🔊 1.27 **Listen, say, and do.**   3 **Find the correct letters and color the picture.**   4 **Trace or color the letter.**
Vocabulary: kite

f   i   j   l

1 🔊 1.28 **Listen and chant.**   2 🔊 1.29 **Listen, say, and do.**   3 **Follow the maze and find the correct letter.**   4 **Trace or color the letter.**
Vocabulary: leg

I can read   leg

1 Say the letter sounds.   2 🔊 1.30 Listen and say the words. Match.   3 Color the objects with the same color.   4 Trace the letters.   5 🔊 1.31 Listen and read.

Vocabulary: juice, kite, leg, **lake**, **key**, jump

Unit 4
Letters j, k, l

19

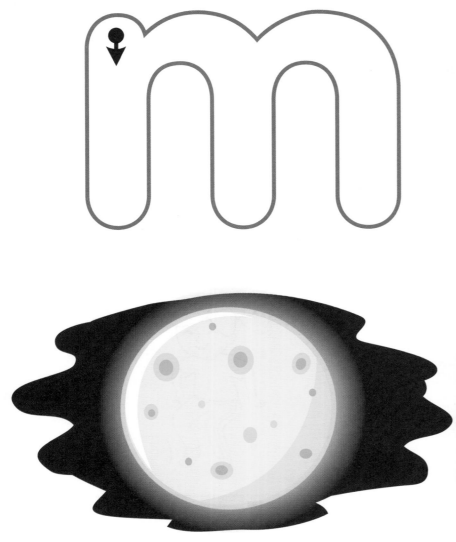

Unit 5
Letter m

1 🔊 1.32 **Listen and chant.** 2 🔊 1.33 **Listen, say, and do.** 3 **Find the correct letters and circle.** 4 **Trace or color the letter.**

Vocabulary: moon

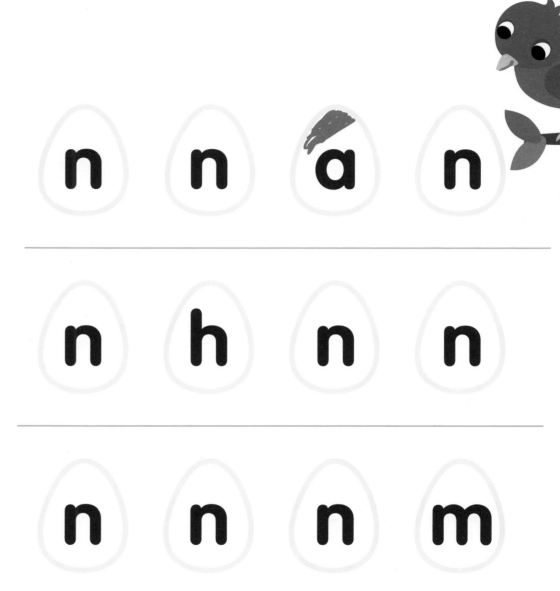

n n a n

n h n n

n n n m

1 🔊 1.34 Listen and chant.　2 🔊 1.35 Listen, say, and do.　3 Find and color the odd one out.　4 Trace or color the letter.

Vocabulary: nest

Unit 5
Letter n

21

Unit 5
Letter o

Vocabulary: octopus

1 🔊 1.36 **Listen and chant.**   2 🔊 1.37 **Listen, say, and do.**   3 **Find the correct letters and color.**   4 **Trace or color the letter.**

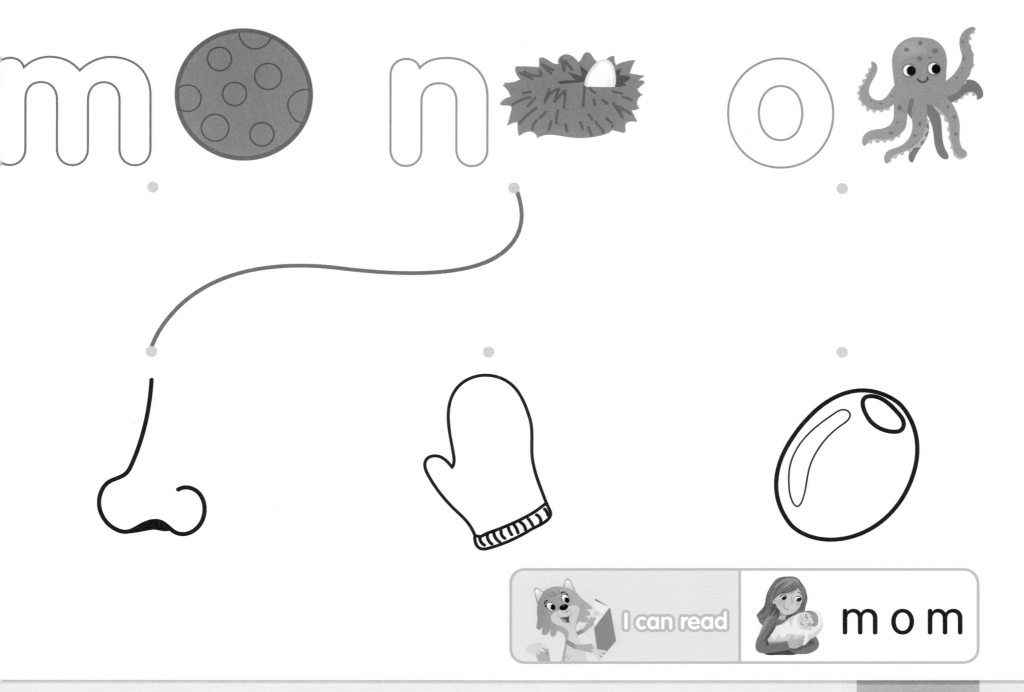

I can read **m o m**

1 **Say the letter sounds.**   2 🔊 1.38 **Listen and say the words. Match.**   3 **Color the objects with the same color.**   4 **Trace the letters.**   5 🔊 1.39 **Listen and read.**

Vocabulary: moon, nest, octopus, nose, mitten, **olive**, mom

Unit 5
Letters m, n, o

23

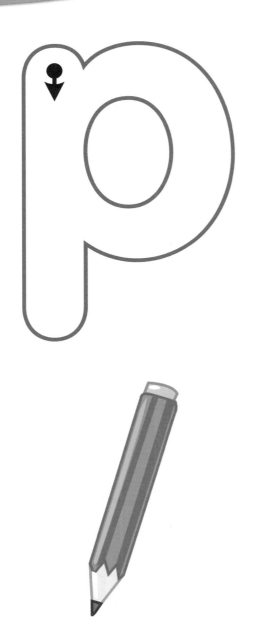

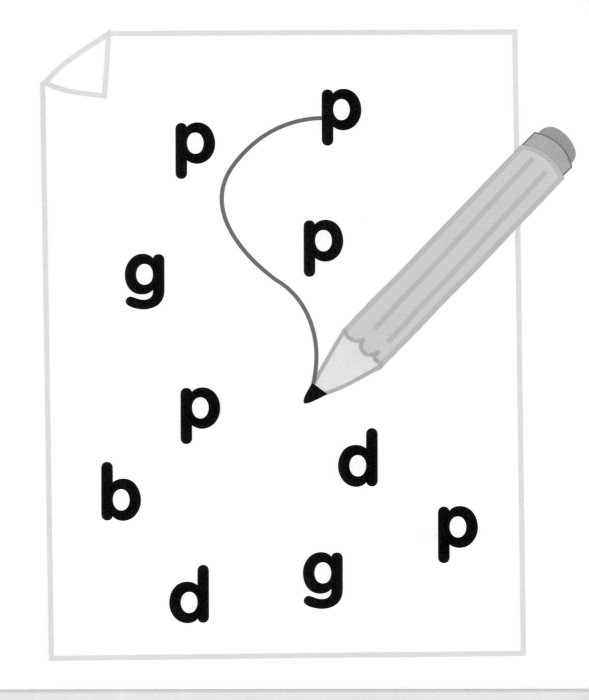

Unit 6
Letter p

1 🔊 1.40 **Listen and chant.**   2 🔊 1.41 **Listen, say, and do.**   3 **Find the correct letters and match.**   4 **Trace or color the letter.**

Vocabulary: pencil

1 🔊 1.42 **Listen and chant.**   2 🔊 1.43 **Listen, say, and do.**   3 **Find the correct letters and color.**   4 **Trace or color the letter.**
Vocabulary: quilt

Unit 6
Letter q   **25**

1 1.44 **Listen and chant.**   2 1.45 **Listen, say, and do.**   3 **Follow the maze and find the correct letter.**   4 **Trace or color the letter.**

Vocabulary: rabbit

I can read

red

1 **Say the letter sounds.** 2 ◆))) 1.46 **Listen and say the words. Match.** 3 **Color the objects with the same color.** 4 **Trace the letters.** 5 ◆))) 1.47 **Listen and read.**
Vocabulary: pencil, quilt, rabbit, **queen**, **rain**, **pizza**, red

Unit 7

1 🔊 1.48 Listen and chant. 2 🔊 1.49 Listen, say, and do. 3 Find the correct letters and match. 4 Trace or color the letter.
Vocabulary: sun

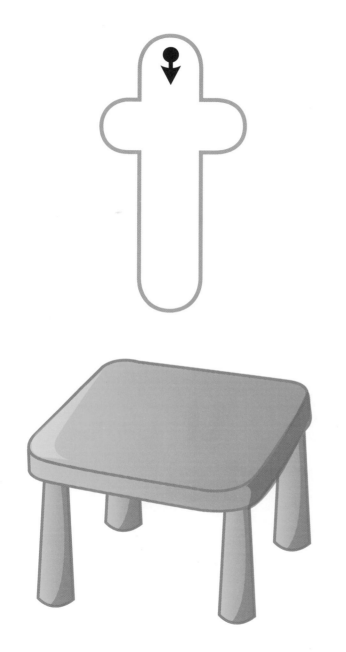

1 ◀)) 1.50 **Listen and chant.**   2 ◀)) 1.51 **Listen, say, and do.**   3 **Follow the maze with the correct letters.**   4 **Trace or color the letter.**
Vocabulary: table

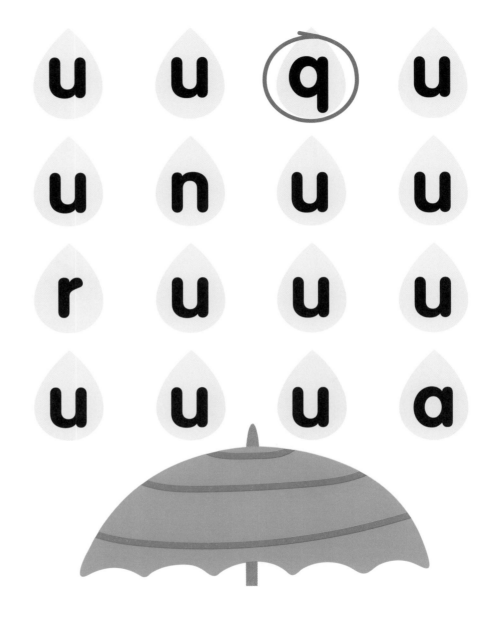

Unit 7
Letter u

1 🔊 1.52 **Listen and chant.**   2 🔊 1.53 **Listen, say, and do.**   3 **Find and circle the odd one out.**   4 **Trace or color the letter.**
Vocabulary: umbrella

I can read

sun

cat

1 Say the letter sounds.   2 1.54 Listen and say the words. Match.   3 Color the objects with the same color.   4 Trace the letters.   5 1.55 Listen and read.
Vocabulary: sun, table, umbrella, **turtle**, **seed**, **up**, cat

Unit 7
Letters s, t, u

31

Unit 8
Letter v
Vocabulary: van

1 🔊 1.56 Listen and chant.   2 🔊 1.57 Listen, say, and do.   3 Follow the maze with the correct letters.   4 Trace or color the letter.

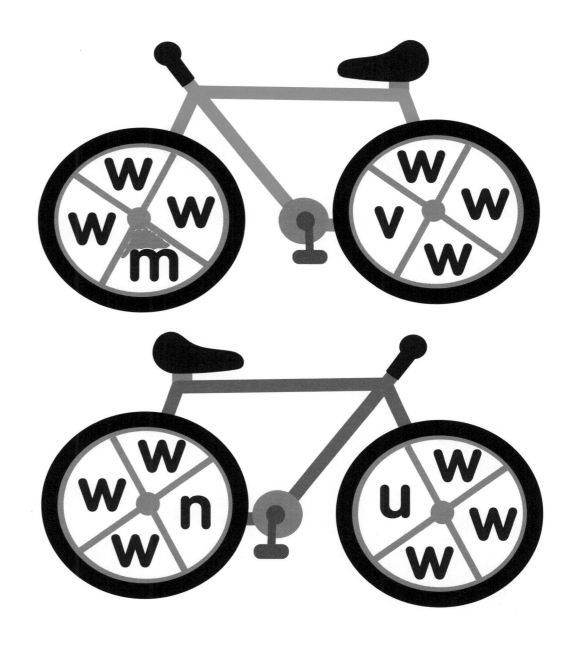

1 🔊 1.58 **Listen and chant.**   2 🔊 1.59 **Listen, say, and do.**   3 **Find and color the odd one out.**   4 **Trace or color the letter.**
Vocabulary: wheel

Unit 8
Letter w

33

 **X** **V** **X** **V** **X**

 **X** **W** **X** **W** **X** **W**

 **X** **V** **W** **X** **V** **W** **X** **V**

Unit 8
Letter x

1 🔊 1.60 **Listen and chant.**   2 🔊 1.61 **Listen, say, and do.**   3 **Trace the next letter.**   4 **Trace or color the letter.**
Vocabulary: fox

I can read   van   6 six

1 **Say the letter sounds.**   2 🔊 1.62 **Listen and say the words. Match.**   3 **Color the objects with the same color.**   4 **Trace the letters.**   5 🔊 1.63 **Listen and read.**

Vocabulary: van, wheel, fox, box, water, **violin**, six

Unit 8
Letters v, w, x

35

Unit 9

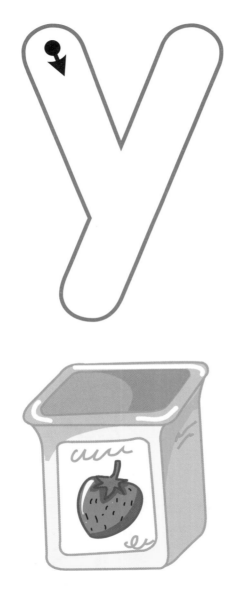

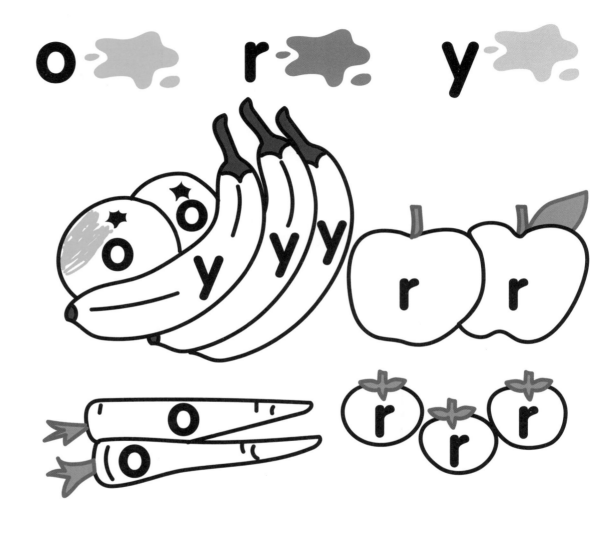

Vocabulary: yogurt

1 1.64 **Listen and chant.**   2 1.65 **Listen, say, and do.**   3 **Find the correct letters and color.**   4 **Trace or color the letter.**

b   e   t   z

1 ◀)) 1.66 **Listen and chant.**   2 ◀)) 1.67 **Listen, say, and do.**   3 **Find and match.**   4 **Trace or color the letter.**

Vocabulary: zoo

bag

sun

ten

hop

·ten

·bag

·hop

·sun

Unit 9
CVC words

1 Find the words and match. 2 🔊 1.68 **Listen and check.** 3 **Trace the words.**
Vocabulary: bag, sun, ten, hop

hat

box

cat    **run**

fox   **sun**

1 **Read and circle.**　2 🔊 1.69 **Listen and check.**　3 **Trace the words.**
Vocabulary: hat, cat, fox, box, **run**, sun

Great Clarendon Street, Oxford, OX2 6DP, United Kingdom

Oxford University Press is a department of the University of Oxford.
It furthers the University's objective of excellence in research, scholarship,
and education by publishing worldwide. Oxford is a registered trade
mark of Oxford University Press in the UK and in certain other countries

ISBN: 978 0 19 405479 9

Printed in China

This book is printed on paper from certified and well-managed sources

ACKNOWLEDGEMENTS

Back cover photograph: Oxford University Press building/David Fisher

Cover artwork by: Rob McClurkan/Bright Agency and
Mike Garton/Bright Agency (in the style of Rob McClurkan)

Main illustrations by: Amanda Enright/Advocate Art

Other illustrations by: Mike Garton/Bright Agency (in the style of Rob Mclurkan):
pp.3 (Fifi), 4 (tree), 6, in the style of Amanda Enright, 7 (bus, red cat, coat only)
in the style of Amanda Enright, 23 (Fifi), 27 (Fifi), 31 (Fifi), and 35 (Fifi)

GUIDE TO CHINESE BRUSH PAINTING

BY ZHENG ZHONGHUA

CYPI PRESS

CONTENTS

INTRODUCTION

Double-outline Bamboo
Li Kan, Yuan Dynasty
Hanging scroll, ink and color on silk
h: 163.5 cm w: 102.5 cm
Palace Museum (Beijing)

Commonly known as "national painting," traditional Chinese painting differs from other schools such as western oil painting and watercolor painting, and exists as an independent category featuring distinctive Oriental flavor. The notion of Chinese painting actually came into being after the Republic Era, before which painting was terms as *"Danqing"* (literally translated as red and blue painting). After this period, western paintings started to gain influence and a lot of Chinese started to learn typical techniques for oil painting and watercolor painting. In this context, Chinese painting started to be celebrated as a local concept distinct from western paintings. Generally speaking, this term refers to the school in which painters employ the brush as the tool. Traditional Chinese paintings can produce a flexible and diversified interpretation of ink and color. Nowadays, traditional Chinese paintings have become recognized across the globe. Increasingly, more and more westerners have started to study it.

Court Ladies Adorning Their Hair
with Flowers
Zhou Fang, Tang Dynasty
Handscroll, ink and color on silk
h: 46 cm w: 180 cm
Liaoning Provincial Museum
(Shenyang)

Listening to the Zither
Zhao Ji, Northern Song Dynasty
Hanging scroll, ink and color on silk
h: 147.2 cm w: 51.3 cm
Palace Museum (Beijing)

Actually, it is not as challenging as we may expect to learn the traditional Chinese painting. After all, compared with its western counterpart, Chinese painting is not focused on reproducing objects in the real world on the paper in an accurate way. Therefore, those who know nothing about perspective can also produce amazing work as long as they are willing to make careful observations, practice in an industrious way, and unbridle their imagination; while those with special training in western painting will make more impressive performance in this field.

However, it still involves certain difficulties if one wants to make an outstanding painter. The most difficult part is that traditional Chinese painting is concerned with other things in addition to capturing what objects really look like. These things belong to the spiritual realm, and can only be visualized by traditional Chinese painting techniques. The masterpieces of traditional Chinese painting are valued due to the spiritual implications embedded within. Traditional Chinese painting observes certain spiritual implications and distinctive approaches to make these implications visible. It differs from its western counterpart in this sense. For example, the latter is mainly focused on subjects such as history, figure and scenery, while the most common subjects in the former category include plum, orchid, bamboo and chrysanthemum.

These four plants are celebrated as the "Four Gentlemen." For over two thousand years, all the painters in dynastic China had studied hard to draw these subjects. The Chinese prefer to paint them not only because they are visually appealing, but also because they represent lofty morality. Many painters are actually thinking of themselves when painting these plants. They are striving to give expression to their ideals and sing praise of their virtues.

Therefore, beginners in traditional Chinese paintings are advised to start with the "Four Gentlemen." When working on these subjects, we should take serious thought of what are embedded in them and what are valued in traditional Chinese paintings. It is commonly recognized that one can constantly refine their character by engaging themselves in traditional Chinese painting. When working on them, the painters can ruminate on profound understandings of life.

This book showcases over two hundred examples, and observes a gradual increase in difficulty. As a beginner in traditional Chinese painting, you will find yourself more and more proficient by finishing this book from cover to cover and making industrious practice. If you have had training or experience in western painting, or have been exposed to Chinese paintings, you can be equally rewarded by reading this book. It is hoped that this book will act as a trustworthy companion; it is also hoped that readers can truly experience the special charm and tranquility defining Chinese painting and use the brush to pursue spiritual pleasure. Readers can also gift their paintings to friends or family and share with them this pleasure.

MATERIALS AND TECHNIQUES

The Scholar's Desk

"One can do nothing without the necessary implements." One should purchase a set of handy implements before starting to learn Chinese brush painting. Chinese attach great importance to these implements, referring them as "the Four Treasures of Study," which include brush, ink, paper and inkstone. For the Chinese, these four treasures are not only functional implements but also a crystallization of the time-honored Chinese culture and its national inspiration. Sometimes, these implements themselves can be exquisite works of art in their own right.

In "*Emperor Qianlong Taking Pleasure*," the man in the painting was actually Emperor Qianlong of the Qing Dynasty. In front of him are the "Four Treasures of Study."

Xuanzhi and Paperweight

Xuanzhi paper dates back to the Tang Dynasty, and earned its name because it was original produced in Xuan City in Anhui Province. As thin as a cicada's wings, it is light but not easy to tear. Water and ink can produce a rich variety of images on its surface. Due to its special properties, it is indispensable in traditional Chinese paintings; it is the only medium which can demonstrate the unique effect of Chinese paintings.

Xuanzhi paper is made of natural materials, including wingceltis bark,

Raw *xuanzhi*

Half-ripe *xuanzhi*

Ripe *xuanzhi*

straw, as well as mulberry timber, fiber and bamboo. The technique to produce *xuanzhi* paper is quite complicated, involving eighteen procedures such as immersing, lime covering, steaming and boiling, bleaching, pulping, rinsing, gluing and sticking. Generally speaking, it takes a whole year to produce *xuanzhi* paper.

The *xuanzhi* paper features a rich variety, and is roughly categorized into raw *xuanzhi*, half-ripe *xuanzhi* and ripe *xuanzhi* based on their ability to absorb water.

Raw *xuanzhi* presents an outstanding performance in absorbing water. Ink will blur in a quick way on such paper and produce various changes. Ink-splashing and ink-accumulating techniques apply to raw *xuanzhi* paper. Generally speaking, raw *xuanzhi* paper should be considered for paintings of landscape and flower-and-bird, as well as figure paintings featuring the "big free style."

The half-ripe *xuanzhi* paper is not as good as raw *xuanzhi* but better than ripe *xuanzhi* at absorbing water. Ink can blur to a certain extent. However, the blurring effect is less evident and more controllable. This kind of paper is mostly used for paintings featuring the small free style and a combination of free style and realistic style.

Ripe *xuanzhi* paper is produced by coating the raw *xuanzhi* paper with alum. The paper is a little harder in texture and worse at absorbing water. The beauty of the paper is that the ink will not blur on paper. More controllable, it is suitable for the realistic-style paintings. However, the setback is that such paper cracks in easily and cannot be stored for a long time.

TIP

Beginners are advised to choose the type that is further processed, on which ink will not easily disperse in an uncontrollable way.

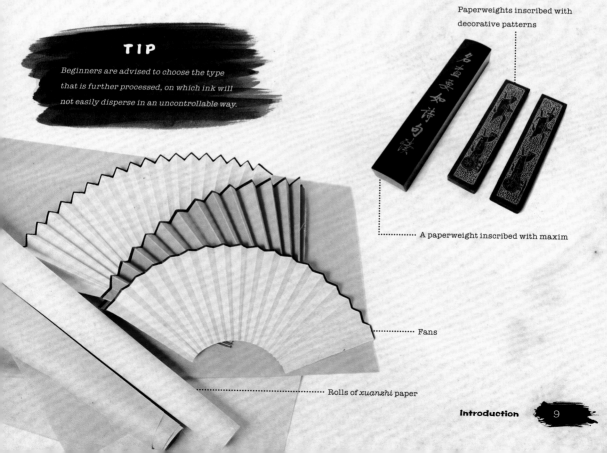

Paperweights inscribed with decorative patterns

A paperweight inscribed with maxim

Fans

Rolls of *xuanzhi* paper

Brush and Brush Holder

The brush is the traditional writing implement in China, and is also indispensable for learning traditional Chinese paintings. Its head is usually made from the hair of various animals such as the rabbit, goat, weasel, and wolf, while its body is made from bamboo, wood, ceramics and other materials. Weasels and wolves are rare now, so the hair from the tip of the dog's tail is a common substitute. Rabbit and goat hair is relatively soft. Thus, brushes made of this hair are referred to as "soft brushes." In contrast, wolf, weasel and dog hair is relatively tough, and can be made into a "tough brush." Generally speaking, beginners are advised to use a "blended-bristled brush," which is made of a mixture of dog's hair and goat's hair, elastic yet stiff.

Based on the shape and length of the bristles, the brush can be categorized into round-tipped, sharp-tipped, long-bristled, medium-bristled, and short-bristled. Generally speaking, the round-tipped and medium-bristled brush is the optimal choice for painters, especially the beginners.

Most traditional Chinese painters keep a brush supporter in their studio. In this way, the brush loaded with water can lean against the stand without staining the desk or paper. In addition, if you have many brushes, it is advised to purchase a brush hanger so that the brush washed clean can hang there until the bristles dry, which will help to make the brush more durable.

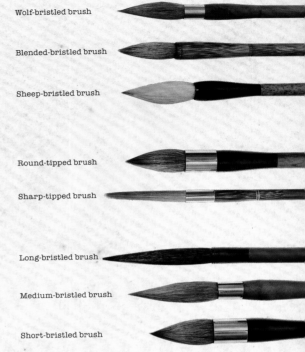

Wolf-bristled brush

Blended-bristled brush

Sheep-bristled brush

Round-tipped brush

Sharp-tipped brush

Long-bristled brush

Medium-bristled brush

Short-bristled brush

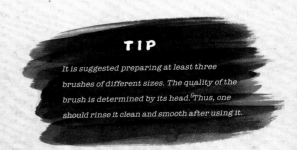

TIP

It is suggested preparing at least three brushes of different sizes. The quality of the brush is determined by its head. Thus, one should rinse it clean and smooth after using it.

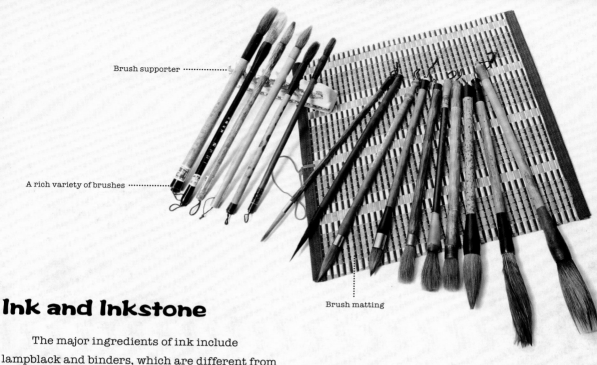

Brush supporter

A rich variety of brushes

Brush matting

Ink and Inkstone

The major ingredients of ink include lampblack and binders, which are different from that for fountain pens. Traditional ink takes the form of ink sticks, which must be rubbed with water on an inkstone to make writing or painting ink. The best ink comes from Anhui, which is home to many ink-producing masters. Their product is not simply an implement for calligraphy or painting, but is a work of art in itself, and can be astonishingly expensive. Nowadays, bottled ink is available, which is easier and less time-consuming to use. However, many people still consider it a joy to rub the ink stick to produce ink.

TIP

If you feel it too troublesome to rub your own ink, you can buy bottled ink instead. Brands such as "Yidege" and "Caosugong" are recommended.

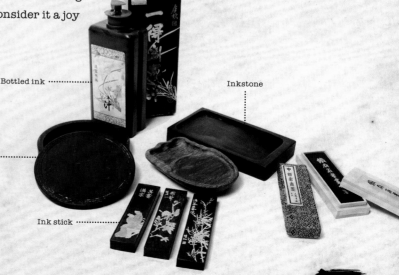

Bottled ink

Inkstone

Inkstone with a cover

Ink stick

Ink and Paint Tray

Paints for traditional painting are generally categorized into ore paint and floral paint. The former category includes cinnabar (vermillion), mineral yellow, mineral green and ochre (brown), while the latter category encompasses cyanine and rouge. Through observation, you will find those is a huge difference between the paint and pigment of Chinese painting and those for oil painting. There is a limited range of paint for Chinese painting, which will, however, produce a wide range of color when mixed together. In modern times, some well-known painters have experimented with applying oil paints to Chinese paintings, whose innovations are well-received.

White ceramic is an optimal material for paint trays, because the material can give a perfect foil to the color of the paints for traditional Chinese paintings, which makes it easier for observation. Besides, the white ceramic features fine texture, which makes it difficult for the paint to dissolve into the tray, making it easier to wash.

TIP

A professional paint tray can be replaced by a white dish tray, which is also practiced by many masters in traditional Chinese painting. It is advised that beginners should choose tubed paints. The Mali paints produced by Shanghai Mali Pigment Factory are also an established brand in the Chinese market.

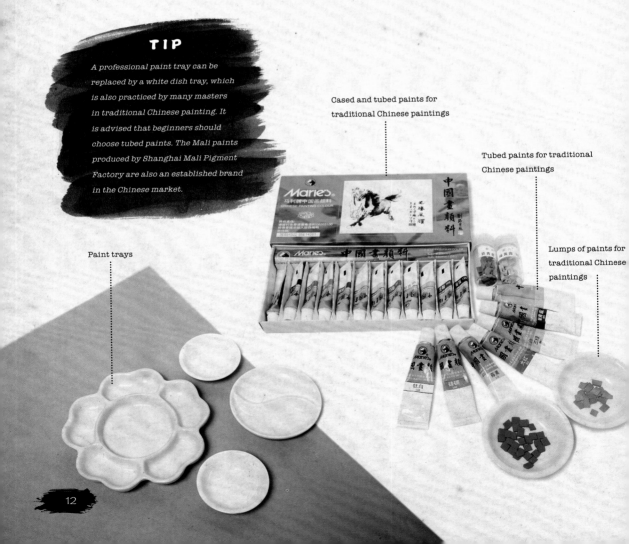

Cased and tubed paints for traditional Chinese paintings

Tubed paints for traditional Chinese paintings

Lumps of paints for traditional Chinese paintings

Paint trays

Brush Washer and Wash Jet

Brush washer and wash jet are both used as water containers. The former has a larger volume because it requires a considerable quantity of water to rinse the brush clean. The latter one has a small volume, and is used to add water into the ink stone or paint tray during the ink-rubbing and color-mixing process. It is usually attached with a filler or a spoon for adding water. Both are exquisitely made to please the user in an aesthetic way when placed on the desk.

Brush washer

Wash jar   Wash jet

Wash spoon

Holding the Brush

Gesture is a key issue when studying traditional Chinese painting. Painters are asked to stay taught with an erect back. When working on large-size Chinese paintings, the elbow and wrist should be suspended in the air. As for small-size paintings, we can rest the arm gently on the desk. Painters should hold the brush by pinching with thumb and index finger one third the length from above, curling the middle finger and leaning it against the ring finger. When moving the brush, we should depend on the strength and movement of the elbow and wrist to lead the brush on the paper. The techniques to hold the brush are relatively complicated. Some beginners might find the movement awkward, but will feel more comfortable after some practice.

Suspending the elbow

Suspending the wrist

Resting the wrist

Grinding the Ink

If using ink sticks rather than bottled liquid ink, we have to grind the ink before starting to paint.

1 Remove the dust on the ink stick before the grinding process. Drip several water drops into the ink stone.

2 Then, grind the ink stick in a gentle way by moving in a single direction.

3 Add more water during the process. We cannot stop until the ink looks thick and even.

There was a saying that ink had five colors in ancient China. Through different proportions of ink and water, we can come up with ink of different hues. Therefore, traditional Chinese painters can create a diverse world solely by using ink.

Loading the Brush

Though seemingly easy on the surface, loading the brush actually involves a lot of consideration.

1 Dip the brush in water and soak the bristles thoroughly. The unused brush has glue on the bristles. We have to immerse them in water and rub them by hand in a gentle way until the glue dissolves.

2 Remove excessive water by scraping the brush against the edge of the washer.

3 At this stage, we can load the brush with ink by rolling the bristles in ink to ensure an even distribution of ink. It should be remembered not to scrape the brush too hard against the ink stone.

4 In the end, scrape the brush gently against the end of the ink stone to squeeze out excessive ink.

Moving the Brush

How to move the brush is the key in traditional Chinese painting. We can utilize various approaches to move the brush when working on traditional Chinese paintings. Generally speaking, if we move the brush in a swift way, the ink will not quickly disperse. Therefore, the strokes will look determined and forceful. On the contrary, slow movement of the brush will cause concentration of ink and produce steady and composed strokes. In traditional Chinese paintings, we use special terms such as "non-tilting" and "tilting" techniques to indicate whether to tilt the brush when moving it.

Non-tilting techinque

Tilting technique

The "non-tilting" technique is the most fundamental approach to moving the brush, and is widely applied in traditional Chinese painting. The defining feature for this technique is that the brush remains vertical with the paper, with only the tip touching the paper. Such a technique will produce forceful strokes.

Tilting technique involves tilting the brush and using the side of the bristles to touch the paper. This technique will produce gentle strokes.

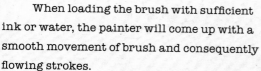

When loading the brush with sufficient ink or water, the painter will come up with a smooth movement of brush and consequently flowing strokes.

If the ink and water in the brush are meager, we will feel the friction as we move the brush, and the strokes will feature many pauses.

Outstanding traditional Chinese painters can fully grasp how much water and ink to load in the brush and utilize either smooth flows or pauses to create amazing effects.

It is advised that beginners should practice and experiment with various techniques to move the brush on paper before studying distinctive genres and certain subjects to familiarize themselves with varied effects and styles produced by different strokes. The more the beginners practice, the better they will find themselves in traditional Chinese painting. It is important to grasp all the techniques to move the brush and the effects these techniques produce.

Techniques

The Chinese attach great importance to techniques, which make up rich variety. The most common techniques include outlining, chapping and dyeing techniques. These three techniques are employed in different conditions and feature distinctive advantages and disadvantages. Generally speaking, the outlining technique applies to figure paintings, chapping technique for landscape paintings and dyeing technique for flower-and-bird paintings. However, these three techniques are interrelated. Only by combining these three techniques in a flexible way can we produce outstanding paintings.

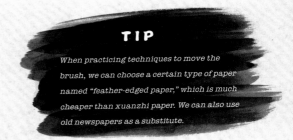

TIP

When practicing techniques to move the brush, we can choose a certain type of paper named "feather-edged paper," which is much cheaper than xuanzhi paper. We can also use old newspapers as a substitute.

Outlining

The outlining technique refers to drawing the contour and structure of the objects. Outlining is one of the fundamental techniques in traditional Chinese painting. When using the outlining techniques, we should ensure two points: one is the smooth flow in strokes, while the other is the accurate structure. Only by ensuring these two points can we fully grasp the outlining techniques. There are certain categories in Chinese paintings such as realistic paintings that are solely based on outlining techniques. Other categories also somewhat depend on the outlining techniques. If a certain painter is not doing well at outlining, he is doomed to fail in the application of chapping and dyeing techniques.

Chapping

The chapping technique is commonly applied in figure and landscape paintings to capture the texture and illumination. When employing the chapping technique, we will usually use light and dry ink; tilt the brush and move it in a swift way. Actually, there is a rich variety of chapping techniques in traditional Chinese paintings, such as the so-called big-ax chapping, small-ax chapping, fiber-chapping and raindrop-chapping, among others.

Dyeing

Dyeing involves coloring the subjects with ink or paint with a higher proportion of water. By using the dyeing technique, we will get even or gradient effects. Generally speaking, the dyeing technique is based on outlining and chapping. When drawing landscape paintings, the painters usually start by outlining the contour of the rocks and then capture their textures by using the chapping technique. In the end, the dyeing technique is used to color the stones with dark green and light ochre.

Mixing Colors

Learning how to mix colors is one of the indispensable processes in learning traditional Chinese painting. Some colors cannot be bright unless blended together with other colors. However, this blending rule does not apply to all cases—some colors might turn dark and dim when blended. Actually, the rules to mix colors in traditional Chinese paintings are almost identical to those applied in watercolor paintings. For those who are new to traditional Chinese painting but have some training in watercolor paintings, it will not be difficult for them to grasp the principles to mix colors. However, there are still variations due to the distinctive properties and color tendencies of the paints. Therefore, it is advised that beginners should blend only two of the paints on the palette. Once familiar with the color changes that result from the blending process, you can start to learn painting techniques.

1 Here we will use a simple example to illustrate the changes as a result of the blending process. First, mix gamboge and cyanine to create fresh green. This color is an optimal choice to depict tender leaves, grass and vines in the spring.

2 Try adding some crimson and mix the colors in a well-proportioned way. A relatively dark brown will be produced. This color is neither bright nor saturated, and can be applied to some withered bamboo poles and branches.

1 Load a clean brush with yellow paint to the root of the bristles.

2 Remove the excessive paint and dip the brush tip in red paint.

3 Produce a fan-shaped form on the paper. Shake the brush sometimes to produce a wave-shaped contour.

1 Load a clean brush with relatively light green to the middle part of the bristles.

2 Dip the brush tip with slightly dark green.

3 Tilt the brush and move upwards, leaving blanks between strokes.

It is advised that beginners establish a color palette. Record all the blends on the palette in addition to the base colors, which will facilitate a better utilization of color.

In traditional Chinese paintings, we can load the brush with two or three colors at the same time. By using such a brush in a tilted way, we will produce color gradient effects on paper. This technique is commonly applied when drawing bamboo and peonies in a suggestive style. Though these two or three colors are not blended on the palette, they are highly solvent, which means that they will produce an elegant blend on the brush and *xuanzhi* paper. The gradient effect is quite charming. This technique is also considered one of the approaches to mix colors.

MOTIFS

Flowers and Other Plants

Plum

Plum, orchid, bamboo and chrysanthemum are celebrated as the "Four Gentlemen" in China, and represent the lofty virtues which are common pursuits aspired to in China. In deep winter, other flowers surrender to the freezing cold, while plum blossoms bloom vibrantly amidst the winter snow. Their resilience is commonly valued, and represents a resurgent theme in Chinese literature.

 1 The "dotting" method can be applied to draw red plum blossoms.

 2 Make a circle by painting another four dots to make up a petal. Pay attention to their relative sizes.

 3 After the red paint dries, load the pointed brush, and draw some short lines from the center of the blossom outward in a radiating way. Each line is ended with a dot. A plum blossom is thus finished.

By adjusting the relative sizes of the five petals, one can get plum blossoms facing different directions and featuring varied perspectives.

It is easier to draw a plum blossom waiting to bloom.

4 When painting the entire plum tree, use relatively thin ink for the trunk. Later, paint the branches as well as the speckles and knots on the trunk with thick ink. When working on the trunk, make a point to reserve space for the blossoms. Paint flowers on both sides of the branches and trunks. Avoid even arrangement. Add some yellow blossoms to create a desired contrast.

1 When painting white plum blossoms, use outlining techniques. Load the pointed brush with thick ink to draw an arch, which is intended as a petal.

2 Draw five petals one after another. Pay attention to their sizes and connections.

3 Paint the pistils by using the same techniques for blossoms. We can draw a small circle in the center of the blossom, and paint short lines in a radiating way.

4 Use ink of different hues to paint the trunk and branches. When drawing the trunk, we can use a free-style way. The more absurd-looking the branches are, the more beautiful they are deemed. Draw plum blossoms on both sides of the branch. Make a note to draw a collection of blossoms facing different directions and projecting different perspectives. Make some of them in full blossom and others in bud.

Orchid

As one of the "Four Gentlemen," orchids are celebrated for their elegance. They are mostly found in tranquil valleys. Exuding an other-worldly nature, this flower is widely loved and commonly compared with the lofty literati who have no fear of authority and care only about their own cultivation. The most difficult thing about painting orchids is the stroke, which has to be flowing but changing at the same time.

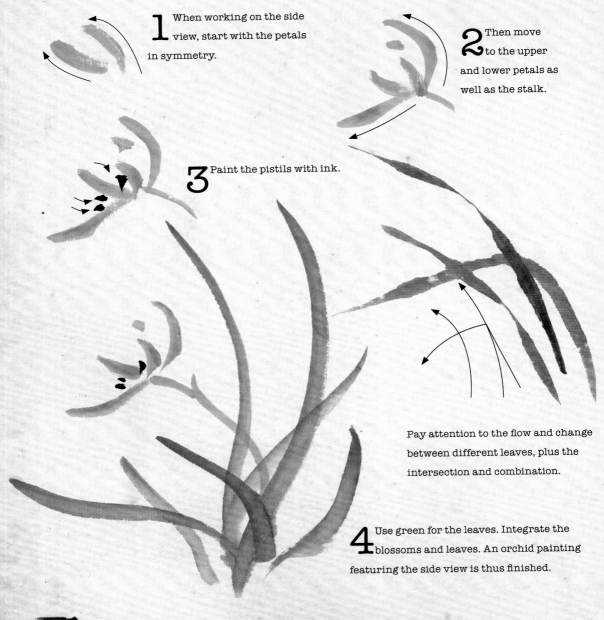

1 When working on the side view, start with the petals in symmetry.

2 Then move to the upper and lower petals as well as the stalk.

3 Paint the pistils with ink.

Pay attention to the flow and change between different leaves, plus the intersection and combination.

4 Use green for the leaves. Integrate the blossoms and leaves. An orchid painting featuring the side view is thus finished.

1 Draw a piece of leaf in one stroke upwards. Avoid evenness and sameness.

2 Paint another two leaves. Avoid parallel arrangement.

3 Integrate several leaves together. Take note of the composition of and intersection between leaves of different poises.

4 The orchid blossom features a special look. Draw a peach-shaped dot, which is intended as the very petal topside.

5 Paint the petals in symmetry, as well as the bag-shaped one beneath.

6 Generally speaking, one stalk of orchid features two to three blossoms. Don't draw too many of them on a single branch, which will threaten to compromise the sense of elegance of this particular flower.

Flowers and Other Plants

Bamboo

In China, bamboo is valued as a plant with integrity. The Chinese started to draw bamboo thousands of years ago. With the booming of literati paintings in the Song and Yuan Dynasties, bamboo evolved into the most significant and common theme in Chinese paintings due to admiration by scholars. It is said that one had to incorporate eight calligraphy techniques to draw the bamboo. In order to produce a satisfactory bamboo painting, it is advised to take time to make a good observation and study the Chinese calligraphy arts.

1 Load the brush with green, and start with the rod. The rod features multiple joints, which are positioned at a closer distance towards the root.

2 Then move to the branch. The branch also has joints on it. Add leaves on both sides of the branch. Make a point of using swift strokes.

3 Load the fine-point brush with thick ink, and outline the rod. Pay attention to the unpainted parts on the joints.

4 Outline the branch and leaves with fine-point brush in thick ink.

5 At the end, add more leaves with ink to contrast with the green leaves to enhance a sense of diversity and depth.

1 The ink painting method is the most time-honored and scholarly one in China. We will take the two-rod bamboo for example here. Start with the leaves and move the brush in a swift way.

2 Add the leaves and the end of the rod. Pay attention to how to move the brush.

3 Add more overlapping leaves by ensuring an orderly style. When working on the combination, make sure that one unit includes two or three leaves. Two leaves are supposed to form up a V-shaped form. When painting the rod, pay attention to the unpainted parts at the joints.

4 Generally speaking, two or three bamboo are enough to make a painting. Pay attention to the interrelationship between the bamboo branches.

Chrysanthemum

Chrysanthemums blossom in autumn. It is a great joy to drink chrysanthemum wines while admiring the beauty of the flower. In traditional Chinese art, chrysanthemum is always associated with seclusive philosophy. Many Chinese paint chrysanthemum to express their desires to shake off all the trivial concerns and obtain absolute freedom. There is a rich variety of chrysanthemum in terms of look and color. Common rare varieties include the lion-headed and golden-hook-and-iron-wire.

1 A chrysanthemum blossom has many petals. Start from those closest to the pistils with saturated red.

2 Apply the same method to draw the petals around the pistils.

3 Use relatively light red for the petals in the periphery.

4 Use ink for the pistils.

5 Generally speaking, one stalk has two to three blossoms, which should be finished with a mixture of cyanine and thin ink. Pay attention to the poise of the leaves.

1 Take note of the poise when applying this method. The clusters in the center are curled inward, which means that the pistils cannot be seen.

2 Work further on the clusters of petals as shown in the illustration.

3 Draw the petals in the periphery with lighter ink layer after layer.

4 Autumn chrysanthemums are mostly golden in color. After the ink completely dries, finish the coloring process in a careful way.

5 Add cyanine and blackish green to thin ink and paint the overall shape of the leaves. When the paint dries, load the fine-point brush with thick ink to outline the veins on the leaves.

Lotus

Lotus is rooted in the mud at the bottom of pond. The Chinese are amazed that the flower which breeds on filthy mud turns out to be elegant and graceful. It is believed that people should learn from lotus by not compromising their decency and loftiness even in harsh conditions. They also compare lotus to a deity due to its beauty.

1 When working on the white lotus, load the brush with ink, and outline the petal. Pay attention to how to move the brush.

2 Combine the petals and create some overlaps. Leave some ink dots as the pistils.

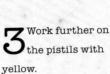

3 Work further on the pistils with yellow.

4 Paint the overall shape with a mixture of thin ink and green paint.

5 Load the fine-point brush with thick ink for the veins.

6 Add the stalk and some tender leaves, and draw the mud and weeds in a suggestive way. A painting of white lotus is thus finished.

1 When working on red lotus, apply a technique of using color lumps to constitute the petal.

2 Two overlapping strokes will make up a petal.

5 The lotus features large leaves which are usually finished by employing the splash-ink technique. In traditional Chinese painting, lotus leaves are usually painted in ink in a suggestive style, black ink equals green paint. Combine the flowers, leaves, seedpods, and stalks by highlighting the flower as the mainstay and taking note of the overlapping relationship between stalks and leaves.

3 Combine several petals of different sizes together. Add the yellow pistils by paying attention to their poise.

4 When drawing the seedpod, load the brush with thick ink for the overall shape. Sketch the seeds with a fine-point brush, and then dye them with ochre.

Candock

Candock and lotus look similar but they are still a little different. The candock flowers and leaves are drifting in the water, while those of the lotus grow out of water. The former prefers strong light, and thus blossoms in the daytime. At night, all the petals will close up, as if falling into sleep, which earns it the name "sleeping beauty" in China. The Chinese have planted candock for many, many years. In the Han Dynasty two thousand years ago, noble people began to use them to decorate their private gardens.

1 Paint a petal in a single stroke. Pay attention to the poise.

2 Add more petals.

3 Leave space for the pistils after having finished all the petals.

4 Use yellow for the pistils.

5 Use ochre for the leaves. We can add a little ink into the paint, and move the brush outward. Ensure that the strokes overlap with each other.

6 A leaf is thus finished.

7 Combine the flower with the leave. Pay attention to the composition. The leaves should be spaced from each other with flowers adding radiance to each other.

1 Apply the outlining technique to draw the candock. Draw a petal in two strokes.

2 Add more petals.

3 Draw the petals behind and beneath.

4 Add the yellow pistils.

5 Draw another candock featuring the overhead view. The petal is finished in two strokes.

6 Draw seven petals in a circle.

7 Add more petals.

8 Draw the pistils.

9 In order to highlight the purity of the candock, use cyanine for the overall shape of the leaf. When the paint dries, sketch the vein and the outline.

Weeping Willow

The Chinese word for "willow" shares a similar pronunciation with that for "stay." Therefore, willow branches were always gifted to travelers who were about to embark on a journey in ancient China, symbolizing people's wish that the travelers would postpone their trips and stay longer. Due to this connotation, weeping willows were favored by both Chinese poets and painters.

2 Paint the willow leaves.

1 Load the brush with light ink, and determine the direction of the drooping branches.

7 When drawing the willow branches, take note of the wind direction.

3 Take note of how the leaves grow on the branch.

4 A willow branch is thus finished.

6 Use different hues for the leaves. However, make sure that the leaves on the same branch are drawn in the same hue. The tender leaves should be lighter in color, and older leaves in a darker color.

5 Start by using light color to determine the directions of the branches.

Reed

Reeds can only survive around water. Widely distributed in China, reeds can be seen on the riverside and lakeside. They usually grow in groves. Reed catkins dance in wind in deep summer, composing a beautiful scene. They were also a resurgent theme in ancient Chinese poems.

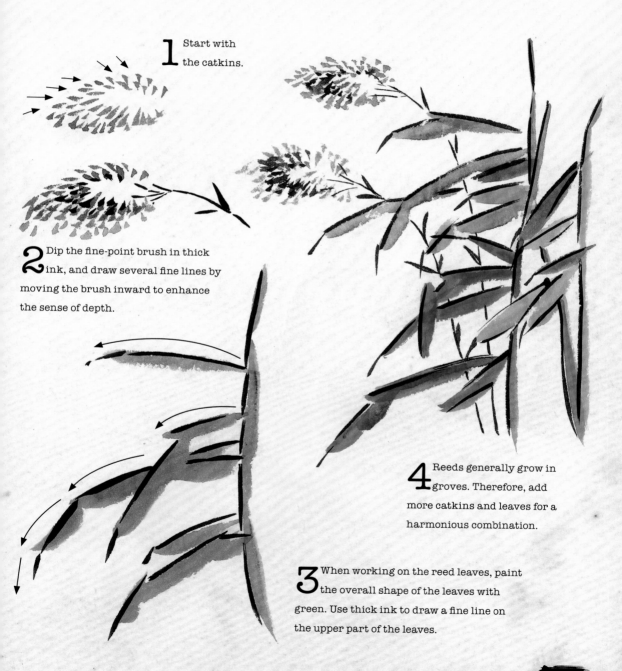

1 Start with the catkins.

2 Dip the fine-point brush in thick ink, and draw several fine lines by moving the brush inward to enhance the sense of depth.

4 Reeds generally grow in groves. Therefore, add more catkins and leaves for a harmonious combination.

3 When working on the reed leaves, paint the overall shape of the leaves with green. Use thick ink to draw a fine line on the upper part of the leaves.

Narcissus

Narcissi mostly grow in water. With an elegant poise and jade-like color, they look just like graceful fairies, which earns them the name "fairies walking over ripples." Exuding a strong fragrance, a bind of narcissi will make the entire room brim over with fragrance when placed on the desk.

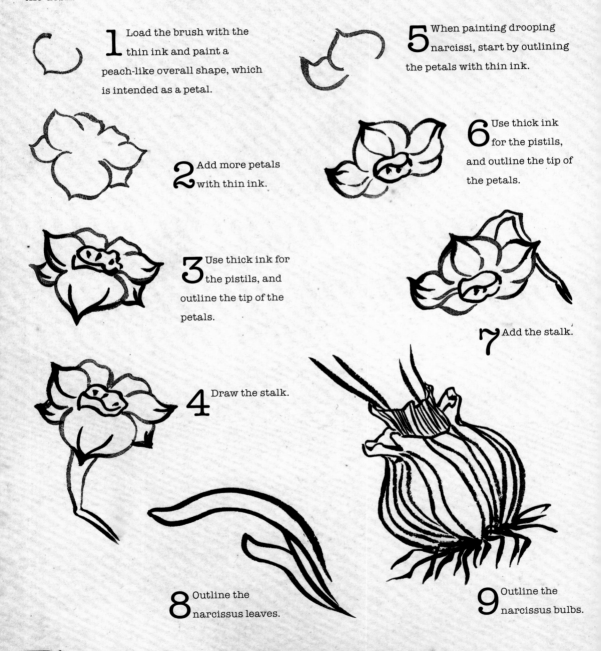

1 Load the brush with the thin ink and paint a peach-like overall shape, which is intended as a petal.

2 Add more petals with thin ink.

3 Use thick ink for the pistils, and outline the tip of the petals.

4 Draw the stalk.

5 When painting drooping narcissi, start by outlining the petals with thin ink.

6 Use thick ink for the pistils, and outline the tip of the petals.

7 Add the stalk.

8 Outline the narcissus leaves.

9 Outline the narcissus bulbs.

10 Combine the blossoms, leaves and bulb by paying attention to the varied perspectives.

Flower-de-luce

Flower-de-luce is greatly favored by Europeans, who usually plant them in their gardens. Ming painters of the Impressionist School also included this flower in their paintings. In China, flower-de-luce is also referred to as "butterfly flower" or "pigeon flower" due to its similar appearance to a butterfly playfully flickering their wings in the flowers, or a pigeon that proudly glides in the sky.

1 It is relatively simple to draw flower-de-luce in bud. Load the brush with bluish violet, and paint an overall shape of a bud in two strokes.

2 Use the grass green for the stalk. Load the fine-point brush with thick ink and draw some tiny and thin lines around the petals, which are intended to capture the grains and drapes of the petals.

3 It is slightly difficult to draw flower-de-luce in full blossom. First start with the petals closer to the pistils with relatively light bluish violet. Six or seven petals are enough.

4 Use relatively dark bluish violet for the petals in the periphery. Draw pistils between the light-colored and dark-colored petals with gamboge.

5 Load the fine-point brush with titanium white, and draw some fine lines on the light-colored petals. Use thin ink for the fine lines on the dark-colored petals.

6 The flower-de-luce features wide leaves. We can add a little cyanine or mineral green to the paint when painting them.

7 Sketch the grain on the leaves with thick ink before the thin ink completely dries.

TIP

It is advised to refer to the flower-de-luce painting by the Impressionist Master Van Gogh to see if there are some inspirations for the traditional Chinese paintings.

8 Combine the blossoms and leaves. A flower-de-luce painting is thus finished. Take note that we should paint the leaves in varied hues to create a sense of depth.

Moth Orchid

We can categorize the moth orchid into many varieties based on color and form. However, all the varieties feature bright colors and robust leaves. In ancient China, the literati preferred the Hanlan and Guolan orchids which are characterized by elegant and light colors plus tender branches and leaves. In modern times, moth orchids of bright and vibrant colors came to be more and more favored by Chinese painters.

1 Load the brush with light ink and draw a wave-edged trumpet.

2 Paint other petals with light ink. Take note that the petal edge is wavy. Use relatively stronger red to fill the mouth of the trumpet.

3 Use light red to dye certain parts of the petal. A moth orchid blossom featuring red, pink and white is thus finished.

Draw the leaves with thin ink in a single stroke, and use thick ink for the veins.

4 Draw two moth orchid blossoms, and add big leaves as a foil. A complete branch of moth orchid is thus finished. Draw the leaf in one stroke, and paint a line in the middle of the leaf as the vein.

1 Apply the outlining method to draw the orange moth orchid. Outline the orchid petals.

2 Sketch the outline of the petals.

3 Use the outlining approach to sketch the drooping moth orchids.

4 Further work on the orchids.

5 Add some details such as the stalks.

6 Draw the leaves as a foil. Use thin ink for the leaves. Combine the outlining method with the "one-stroke" approach to enhance the sense of diversity in the painting.

Begonia

Also known as "heart-broken grass" and "flower of lovesickness" in China, begonia features white frost-like speckles on the leaves, which are said to be the tear stains of a lady who cried at the thought of her husband who was far away from home. In ancient China, it is a tradition to paint begonia and gift the painting to their lovers on a distant land to express their yearnings.

1 Use relatively light rouge to paint begonia. Begonia features clusters of blossoms, plus small and round petals.

2 Pay attention to the composition. Add more petals.

3 Load the brush with light ochre, and paint the tender branches by connecting all the petals.

4 Use light greenish black or light ochre to draw the overall shape of the leaves.

5 Load the fine-point brush with thick ink and paint the veins. In the end, use titanium white to dot the leaves before the paint and ink dry.

6 Combine the leaves with blossoms.

Hydrangea

Hydrangea can be found in China, Japan and Europe. In China, hydrangea stands for eternity and loyalty. The ancient Chinese used to observe a tradition that the girl had to marry the man who caught the silk ball she threw out. Sharing the same name with the "silk ball" in China, hydrangea is thus associated with unchanged love. Hydrangea features large clusters of blossoms, just like the silk ball used in the husband-hunting ceremony in ancient China.

1 Load the brush with light blue or sapphire, and draw four dots for the hydrangea petals.

2 Use ink to dot in the center as the pistils.

3 Apply a mixture of thin ink and turquoise green at random proportions to draw the leaves. Start with an overall shape.

4 Load a fine-point brush with thick ink for the veins.

5 Combine the blossoms and leaves. Clusters of hydrangea blossoms look like balls when observed afar. Take note that blossoms should be related, though with a certain distance in between.

Wisteria

As one of the most revered ornamental flowers of the vine category, wisteria is commonly seen in the courtyards of Chinese residence. From April to May, wisteria blossoms all over the flower shelf. When taking a walk below the shelf and looking at clusters of wisteria, one can feel great joy. Wisteria is a resurgent theme in Chinese paintings. Many painters such as Qi Baishi and Zhang Daqian were famous for painting them.

1 Load the brush with aubergine, and use two strokes to draw something like a hog hoof, which is intended as a petal unit.

2 Add more units and make a cluster. Paint some pine-nut-shaped dots below the units by moving the brush outward.

3 Add two yellow dots below the units. Mix thin ink with a little green to draw the stalks connected with the petals. A wisteria blossom is thus finished.

4 Use thin ink and a little green to draw the leaves. Pay attention to the arrangement pattern. Belonging to the liana category, curly vines are one of the defining features for wisteria.

Morning Glory

Resembling a trumpet in shape, morning glories are commonly known as "trumpet flowers" in China. They are the earliest to blossom in a day, which has earned it a name "laborious lady." When the day breaks at the first crowing, the morning glories are already in full blossom.

1 It is relatively simple to draw morning glory buds. Use blue to draw petals which wrap up together.

2 Load the brush with dark green to paint calyx below the petals.

3 Move the brush inward and paint three strokes with indigo.

4 Add another two indigo strokes, and gradually move the brush inward.

5 Outline the entire trumpet mouth. Use dark green of low concentration for the lower part of the trumpet, dark green for calyx and stalks, and gamboge and thick ink for the pistils.

6 Draw the overall shape of the leaves with dark green.

7 Use thick ink for the veins on leaves.

8 Combine the blossoms and leaves together.

Chinese Hibiscus

Also known as "red hibiscus," Chines hibiscuse is mostly cinnabar in color. In China, they are usually compared to the rising sun. Growing in South China, ancient females in Guangdong always inserted this flower in their hair for adornment.

1 Draw a dot with light cinnabar, which is intended as a petal.

2 Add more petals.

3 Resembling a trumpet in shape, each blossom features five petals. Use gamboge for the pistils.

4 Mix cinnabar of high saturation with ochre to further work on the details of petals and pistils.

5 Load the brush with thick ink and draw two leaves.

7 Use thin ink for some leaves, and some tender branches, which string up the leaves of different hues.

6 Add more leaves.

8 Combine blossoms with leaves. It should be noted that Chinese Hibiscus blossom is never blurred by leaves. Generally speaking, blossoms are closer to the sun than the leaves.

Christmas Flower

It is said that Christmas flowers were originally found in Mexico, and later introduced into China. In modern times, its flaming color impressed Chinese people and they are thus commonly used to celebrate the festivals.

3 Mix ink with a little dark green, and draw the leaves and stalks in a free-hand style.

1 Use crimson to paint the petals, each of which consists of two overlapping strokes.

2 Add more petals. Start from the pistils and move outwards. Use yellow and green for the pistils.

TIP

When working on the leaves and stalks, we should use relaxed and free-style strokes.

Lily

Lilies are commonly used in Chinese wedding ceremonies to express good wish. Its Chinese name "baihe" are short for "bainian haohe," literally translated as "a harmonious union lasting for one hundred years." White lilies are most favored by the newly-weds because their pure color is a crystallization of purity and loyalty for love, known as "cloud-cladded deities."

1 Load a fine-point brush with thin ink to outline the lily petals.

2 When working on the details, draw a line in the middle to present the ridge.

3 Move to the pistils and stalks.

4 Mix dark green and thin ink for the leaves. First start with the overall shape.

5 When the paint dries, load the fine-point brush with thick ink to capture the grains.

6 Combine blossoms with leaves. Generally speaking, a branch is adorned with two to three blossoms.

Calla

Callas are mostly white, but some of them are pink in color. They are always associated with unswerving loyalty. The techniques to draw callas are relatively simple. They are made up of one blossom with two leaves or two blossoms with three leaves. Beginners in traditional Chinese paintings can draw a calla to express their deep passions for their lovers.

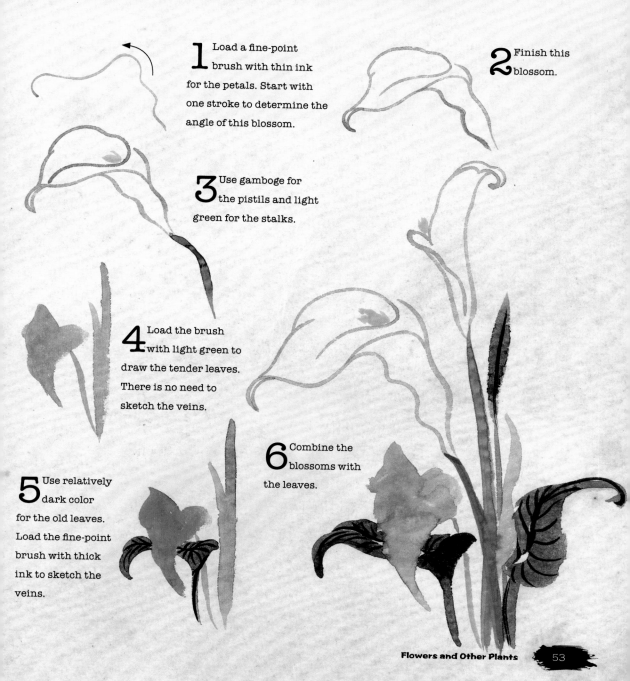

1 Load a fine-point brush with thin ink for the petals. Start with one stroke to determine the angle of this blossom.

2 Finish this blossom.

3 Use gamboge for the pistils and light green for the stalks.

4 Load the brush with light green to draw the tender leaves. There is no need to sketch the veins.

5 Use relatively dark color for the old leaves. Load the fine-point brush with thick ink to sketch the veins.

6 Combine the blossoms with the leaves.

Cineraria

Cineraria was introduced into China and commonly grown in gardens and flower beds because of its growth speed and ability to survive in harsh conditions. In traditional Chinese paintings, we can refer to techniques to draw chrysanthemums when working on cineraria. However, we should also pay attention to the particular forms of its leaves, stalks and buds.

1 Cinerarias mostly feature bright color. Therefore, we use bright orange to draw an oblong for the petal.

2 Add more petals and arrange them in a circle.

3 Use light orange for the pistils, leaving the center unpainted to create a sense of depth and diversity.

4 The leaves share something in common with those of other plants such as towel gourds and watermelons.

5 Cineraria mostly grows in clusters. Take note how leaves interact with blossoms.

Sunflower

Originally growing in North America, sunflowers were introduced into China in the Ming Dynasty. They were initially referred to as "Zhangju" (literally translated as "towering chrysanthemum") but later known as "sunflowers" due to their nature to follow the sun all day along. Sunflowers are used to emblematize the imperial loyalty to the country in ancient Chinese poems. When working on sunflowers, take note of distinguishing between sunflowers and chrysanthemums.

1 Use brown for the pistils. Pay attention to the change in density. The pistils are supposed to be sparse in the center and dense in the periphery.

2 When the brown paint dries, apply light yellow for pistils.

3 Draw petals around the pistils. Use bright yellow to paint petals featuring different poses to make them vivid.

4 Sunflowers feature relatively large leaves. Use dark green and grass green for the overall shape. When the paint completely dries, load the brush with thick ink to draw the veins.

5 Combine the blossoms and leaves. The stalk should be stout enough to support the large blossom.

Magnolia Flower

Chinese people have a deep affection for magnolia flowers, which are grown both in North and South China. It is also the "city flower" for Shanghai. The magnolia tree is leafless when the flowers are in blossom. Large white magnolia flowers contrast with brown branches, exuding intoxicating beauty. Many renowned painters in ancient China, including Chen Hongshou, chose magnolia as their subject.

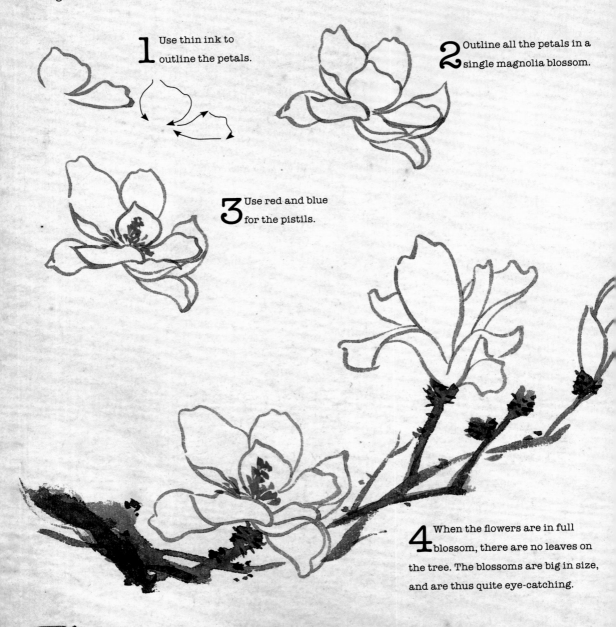

1 Use thin ink to outline the petals.

2 Outline all the petals in a single magnolia blossom.

3 Use red and blue for the pistils.

4 When the flowers are in full blossom, there are no leaves on the tree. The blossoms are big in size, and are thus quite eye-catching.

Camellia

Traditionally known as one of the "Ten Renowned Flowers" in China, camellia comes in a rich variety, exceeding two thousand in number. Based on petal arrangement, we can categorize camellia into the monopetalous and the half-polyphyll categories, as well as those with polyphyll. Relatively speaking, the second and third categories are more complicated to draw. Therefore, we choose to focus on the most basic category — the monopetalous ones.

1 Use bright cinnabar for the petals.

2 Pay attention to the changes in size when drawing the petals.

3 Generally speaking, the monopetalous camellia has five petals.

4 Use gamboge and titanium white for the pistils, and green for the calyx.

5 In order to highlight the blossoms, the leaves are supposed to be drawn in a relatively simple way.

6 Pay attention to the combination of leaves.

7 Combine the blossoms and leaves. Generally speaking, there are three or four blossoms or buds on one branch.

Rose

Roses are always referred to as "flowers of romance." We can apply some traditional Chinese techniques to draw a rose painting. According to historical records, the Chinese originally put roses in small bags for their fragrance. In the Ming Dynasty, Chinese discovered the edibility of roses, and started to use them for wine and tea.

1 Use relatively dark red to paint the petals in the center.

2 Use relatively thin garnet red for the petals in the periphery.

3 When the paint dries, load the brush with thick ink to highlight the structure of petals in the center.

4 Paint the rose leaves in dark green.

5 Add some light colors to enhance the diversity in the painting.

6 Draw the veins with thick ink. Take note that the edge of rose leaves are zigzagging.

7 When drawing the roses, remember to draw the thorns on the branches.

Chinese Rose

Chinese rose shares a similar look with roses, and thus has earned its name. Chinese roses are mostly red, yellow or white in color. Among them, white Chinese roses are associated with dignity and purity. Here, we will mainly talk about how to paint white roses with outlining technique.

2 Just like roses, Chinese roses also feature layers of petals.

1 Load the brush with thin ink and start with the petals in the center.

3 After outlining the petals for the entire blossom, use cinnabar to dot the pistils.

4 Chinese rose leaves are generally drawn in the same way with roses. Use thin ink for the overall shape.

5 Load the fine-point brush with thick ink to draw the veins and the zigzagging edge.

6 Use thick ink to draw some more leaves. Leaves of different hues can enhance a sense of diversity in the paintings.

7 Draw a small cluster of white roses, whose branches are slightly red in color. In traditional Chinese paintings they are also drawn in bright red.

Chinese Banana Tree

Chinese banana tree is one of the most common subjects in traditional Chinese paintings. To the Chinese people, the Chinese banana tree is aesthetically pleasing. Therefore, they often plant them in courtyards, where the flourishing tree contrasts with the grey tiles and white walls. Chinese banana trees make a more intoxicating scene in the rain. Rain beating against the leaves define the ultimate aesthetic expectations in Chinese poems and paintings.

1 Blossoms of Chinese banana trees feature large volume and special shapes. We can use light red to paint them.

2 Dot under the blossoms with green. These green dots will later grow into edible bananas.

3 Use relatively dark red for the grains on the blossoms.

4 It matters a lot what techniques are applied to draw Chinese banana leaves. The quality of a Chinese banana painting is determined by how the leaves look.

5 Draw several parallel strokes to come up with the overall shape of the leaves.

6 When the thin ink dries, use thick ink for the veins on the leaves. Add blossoms below the leaves.

Pine

Pines are green-leaved throughout the year. Some of them can even survive for eight or nine hundred years. It is a time-honored Chinese tradition to use pines to stand for longevity. Chinese people always paint pines together with red-crowned cranes and sometimes give the paintings to aged people, wishing that they could live a long life. When painting pines, we should highlight how towering they are, and demonstrate how they wrestle with winds and snows.

 1 Paint pine needles with thick ink. Make a quick stroke by swiftly moving the brush outward.

 2 Paint one after another pine needle.

 3 Finish one cluster of pine needles.

 4 Combine two clusters together by paying attention to the overlapping relationship.

 5 When working on needles, insert the pine cones.

7 Paint more clusters. When painting the trunk, we should take note of the bark. Use thin ink and the axing techniques first and apply thick ink to perfect the details. A head-down pine is thus finished.

 6 Add more needles around the cones.

Peony

Peonies are valued as the "national flower" in China and have been long deemed to emblematize wealth and auspice because of their elegance. Peonies in Luoyang of Henan are best known throughout China. Travelers are advised to visit Luoyang, the time-honored city, when peonies are in full blossom. Peony is also a common theme in traditional Chinese paintings. However, it is not easy to produce good peony paintings. We should pay attention to how the peony petals overlap with each other.

1 Peonies feature big blossoms and big petals. Therefore, "gradation techniques" are suggested. Load a brush with relatively light red, and paint some petals as the foil. Use relatively strong red to paint another layer of petals before the paint dries.

2 Use stronger red to paint another layer of petals in the periphery.

3 Paint the yellow pistils.

4 Peony leaves are also relatively big. We can draw them with the mixture of ink and cyanine. Take note of the color hues.

5 Combine leaves of different hues together.

6 Use thick ink for the veins, and light ink and brown for the branches.

7 Add more tender leaves and branches as a foil.

9 Add to the tender leaves with buds.

8 Use ochre for tender leaves.

10 Combine the blossoms and leaves. Peonies have a rich variety of colors, including crimson, pink, white, yellow and even dark purple. In the example, we have painted a red one and a yellow one. The contrast between the two is quite use. We should use yellow pistils to match with red blossoms and matching red pistils with yellow blossoms.

Fruits and Vegetables

Cherry

The Chinese always compare a beautiful woman's small mouth to the cherry. Therefore, the cherry is visually pleasing in Chinese aesthetics. The Chinese started to plant and eat the cherry over three thousand years ago. The cherry is a common and relatively simple subject in traditional Chinese paintings. Beginners should start with the cherry.

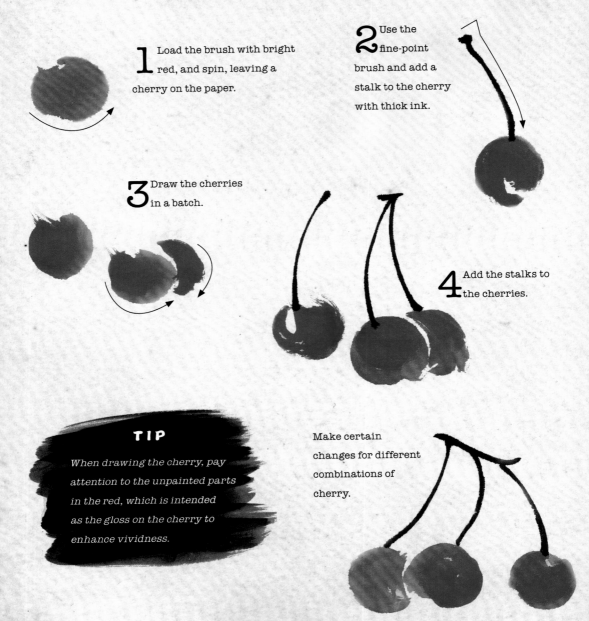

1 Load the brush with bright red, and spin, leaving a cherry on the paper.

2 Use the fine-point brush and add a stalk to the cherry with thick ink.

3 Draw the cherries in a batch.

4 Add the stalks to the cherries.

TIP

When drawing the cherry, pay attention to the unpainted parts in the red, which is intended as the gloss on the cherry to enhance vividness.

Make certain changes for different combinations of cherry.

Strawberry

The strawberry is not only pleasing in look but also delicious in flavor. It is relatively simple to draw.

1 Use a relatively light red for the overall form.

2 When the red dries, use the ink brush to dot the surface and draw the stalk with green.

3 Add more strawberries to make combinations.

Pear

The bright-yellow pear has a pleasing flavor, and can be finished within several strokes.

3 Use thick ink for the stalk and relatively thin ink for the tiny dots on the pear.

1 Load the brush with gamboge and pay attention to the directions of the strokes.

2 Draw the overall form, and take note of the changes in hues. Avoid parallel strokes.

Loquat

As a seasonal fruit, the loquat acts as a messenger for summer. When people see the loquat in the market, they know for sure that the summer is on its way. The loquat tree features flourishing branches and leaves as well as golden fruits. People feel their mouths watering even at the sight of loquat fruits. Therefore, the loquat tree and fruits are common subjects in traditional Chinese paintings.

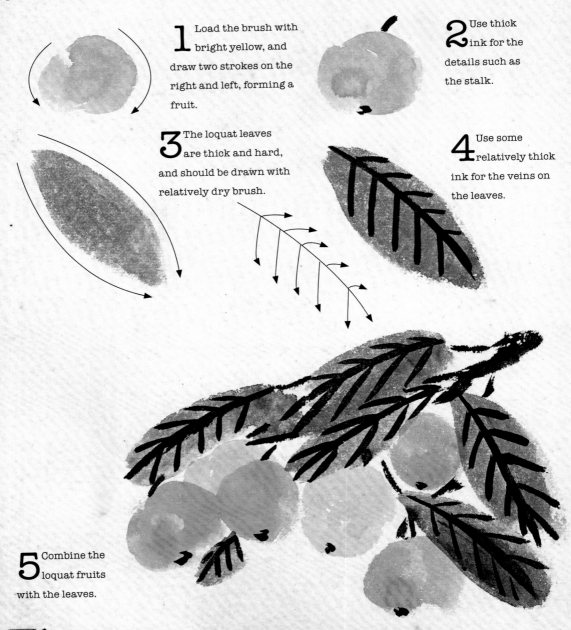

1 Load the brush with bright yellow, and draw two strokes on the right and left, forming a fruit.

2 Use thick ink for the details such as the stalk.

3 The loquat leaves are thick and hard, and should be drawn with relatively dry brush.

4 Use some relatively thick ink for the veins on the leaves.

5 Combine the loquat fruits with the leaves.

Persimmon

The Chinese started to plant the persimmon trees over one thousand years ago. In autumn, the branches will bend at the weight of the orange persimmons, which makes a beautiful scene. The Chinese maintain the persimmon as an emblem of auspice and good harvests. Traditional Chinese paintings themed on the persimmon are one of the best options to gift friends or hang in the house on festive days.

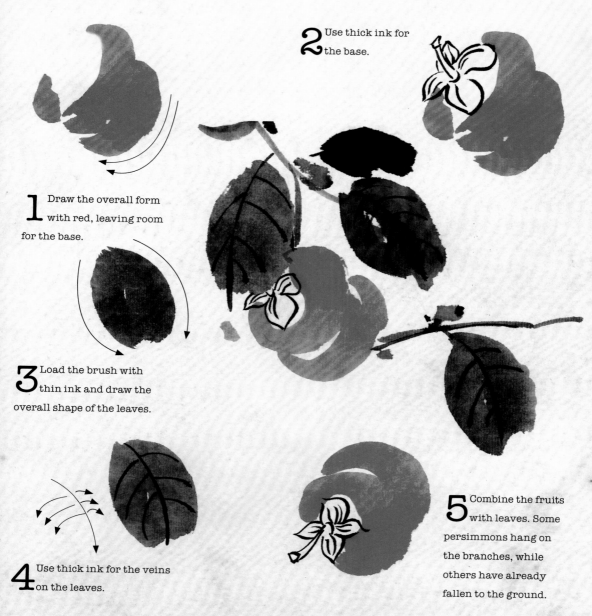

2 Use thick ink for the base.

1 Draw the overall form with red, leaving room for the base.

3 Load the brush with thin ink and draw the overall shape of the leaves.

4 Use thick ink for the veins on the leaves.

5 Combine the fruits with leaves. Some persimmons hang on the branches, while others have already fallen to the ground.

Peach

The peach is always associated with longevity in China. One of the most recognizable features of the God of Longevity is the peach in his hand. Chinese people traditionally made peach-shaped steamed buns or stuffed buns for aged people on their birthday. It is also a good choice to draw a peach painting to gift old people. Wu Changshuo, a modern master of traditional Chinese paintings, painted the peach in a particularly distinctive way.

1 Use yellow to draw the overall shape of the peach. Pay attention to the changes in hues by avoiding parallel strokes.

2 Apply a little red to the point of the peach before the yellow dries. The peach should be redder and redder towards the point.

3 As a foil, the leaves should be small in size. Use thin ink to draw the overall shape.

4 Load the brush with thin ink and draw the veins on the leaves.

5 Combine the fruits with leaves. A painting of double peaches is thus finished.

Plum

As a common fruit in China, the plum is genetically close to the blackberry in North America. However, the former is smaller in size than the latter, with a stronger tinge of purple and red. There is a Chinese saying "the peaches and plums are all over the country," indicating that the teacher has disciples in different parts of the country, contributing by training students for the nation. Therefore, it is one of the best options to gift a teacher a peach and plum painting.

1 Load the brush with red, and spin the brush to the left.

2 Spin the brush to the other side. The two strokes make up a plum.

3 Mix the thin ink with ochre to draw the overall form of the plum leaves.

4 Use thick ink for the veins on the leaves.

5 Combine the fruits with the leaves. Take note of the color variations between different fruits to achieve a sense of vividness.

Eggplant

The eggplant is a common vegetable for the Chinese. With glossy and purple peel, it is a favorite of painters. Round or oval, or even resembling a banana in shape, the eggplant is easy to paint. Therefore, beginners can start with the eggplant.

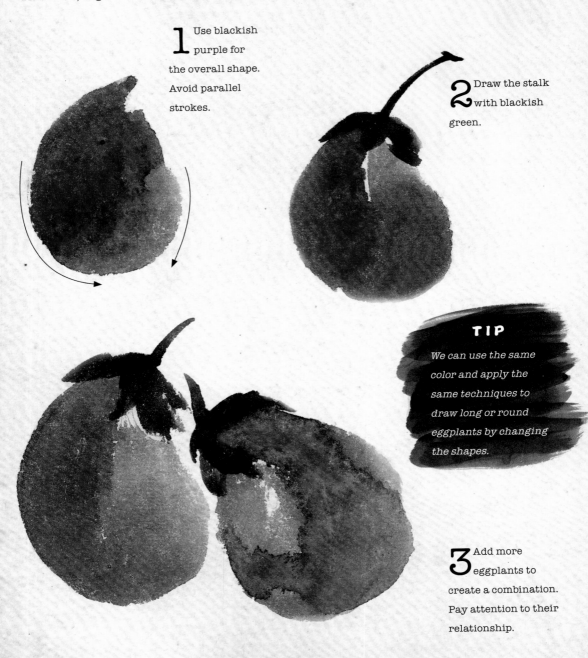

1 Use blackish purple for the overall shape. Avoid parallel strokes.

2 Draw the stalk with blackish green.

TIP

We can use the same color and apply the same techniques to draw long or round eggplants by changing the shapes.

3 Add more eggplants to create a combination. Pay attention to their relationship.

Tomato

The tomato is a common vegetable on the dinner table in modern China. When applying traditional Chinese painting techniques to draw the tomato, we should take care of its special color by adding a little gamboge to cinnabar to give it a semi-transparent tinge.

1 Load the brush with orange.

2 One stroke on the left and one stroke on the right will make up the overall form. Remember to leave the highlighted part unpainted.

3 Use thick ink for the stalk.

TIP

When drawing tomatoes, we can blend yellow and red together to produce orange. Load the tip of the brush with red, and the middle part with yellow so that every single stroke features color gradation. By using this way, the tomato will have a tinge of yellow amid red, which is visually appealing.

Add more tomatoes to make a combination.

Shallot

The shallot plays an important role in Chinese cooking. The Chinese are used to adding seasonings such as shallot, garlic and ginger to boiling oil, which is professionally termed as "*baoxiang*" (literally translated as "let the fragrance explode").

1 Draw a leaf in a single stroke.

2 Add two more leaves. Pay attention to the intersection.

3 After finishing the leaves, use ink to outline the stalk and root.

Green Pepper

The green pepper is relatively simple to draw, and is thus a good option for the beginners to start with.

1 The green pepper actually consists of several vertical sections. Finish each section in a single stroke.

2 Work on the overall form.

3 Add the stalk. A green pepper is thus finished.

Hot Pepper

In Southwest China (such as Hunan and Sichuan Provinces), hot peppers are a favorite for local people. For them, dinner will lose its flavor if the hot pepper is removed. The spicy Hunan and Sichuan cuisines are often quite a challenge for foreigners.

1 Load the brush with red, and finish the overall shape in two strokes. The upper stroke should be wider than the lower one.

2 Use ink for the stalk.

We can draw green hot peppers and red-and-yellow peppers by using different colors.

Garlic

Garlic is an indispensable ingredient in Chinese cooking. It is said that garlic was introduced to China from the Western Region (the vast area east of today's Pamirs Plateau, southeast of the Lake Balkhash and west of Gansu's Dunhuang) by Zhang Qian in the Han Dynasty, who visited the region for a diplomatic mission.

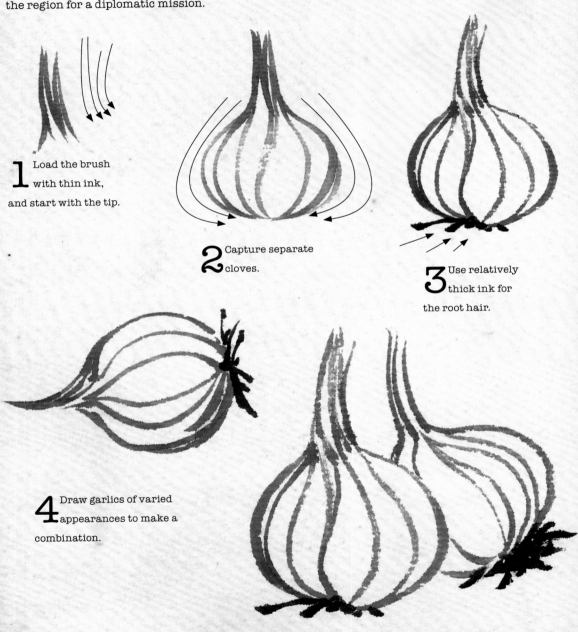

1 Load the brush with thin ink, and start with the tip.

2 Capture separate cloves.

3 Use relatively thick ink for the root hair.

4 Draw garlics of varied appearances to make a combination.

Pumpkin

Bright in color, the pumpkin is a good subject for traditional Chinese paintings. As one of the favorite vegetables in China, the pumpkin can serve both as cuisine or as a substitute for grains. In the countryside, whenever there is a bad harvest of grains, people live on the nutritious pumpkin instead of rice and flour.

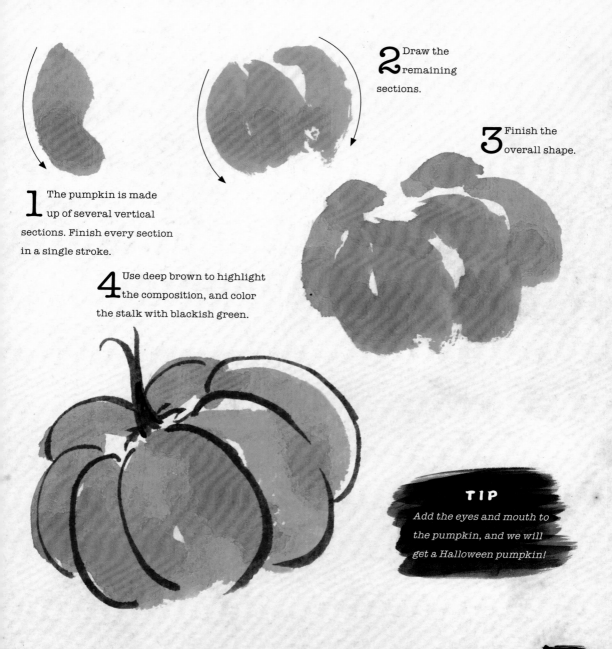

2 Draw the remaining sections.

3 Finish the overall shape.

1 The pumpkin is made up of several vertical sections. Finish every section in a single stroke.

4 Use deep brown to highlight the composition, and color the stalk with blackish green.

TIP

Add the eyes and mouth to the pumpkin, and we will get a Halloween pumpkin!

Watermelon

To the Chinese, the watermelon is an essential companion in summer. It is a great joy for the entire family to share a juicy watermelon in the scorching heat. Besides, the watermelon is also a common subject in modern Chinese paintings. Qi Baishi, a master of Chinese painting, included the watermelon in his paintings.

1 Start with a watermelon which has been cut open. Draw the peel in a single stroke.

2 Work on the red pulp inside.

3 When the red dries, use thick ink to dot the pulp, creating the seeds.

4 An intact watermelon is not difficult to draw. Start with the overall shape in several strokes.

6 In the end, combine the intact watermelon with the one that has been cut open to create an integral whole. People will feel a breath of summer at the sight of your painting.

5 Use ink for the stripes on the peel and the stalk before the paint dries completely.

Carrot

The carrot was introduced to China in the Song and Yuan Dynasties from Afghanistan. The ancient Chinese referred to the region west of Yumenguan Pass and Yangguan Pass (located in the today's Dunhuang in Gansu) collectively as "*Hu* Land," while residents in that region were known as "*Hu* people." Therefore, the carrot which originated from that area was named "Hu radish" in China.

1 It is relatively simple to draw the carrot. Produce a blend of orange which is close to the color of the carrot. Move the brush from left to right.

2 Draw strokes closely togelher.

3 Draw until the tip is obvious. Take note to move the brush downward. The carrot should be thinner and thinner from top to bottom.

4 Use grass green for the stalk.

TIP

When working on the carrot, pay attention to the interrelationship between strokes. The latter one should overlap a little with the former one, but both strokes should be identified as independent strokes.

Red Radish

The red radish is red in peel but transparently white within. It is usually made into a cold dish in Chinese cooking. As one of the favorite vegetables in China, the red radish is commonly cooked in winter. According to the Chinese, the red radish is good for health just like ginseng.

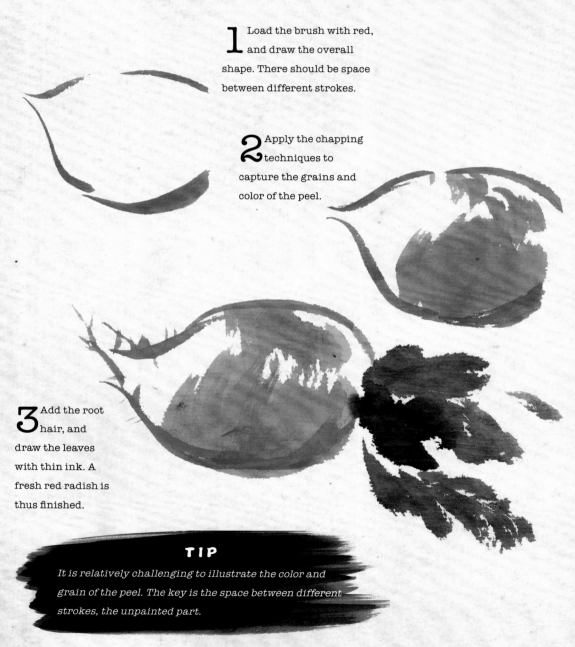

1 Load the brush with red, and draw the overall shape. There should be space between different strokes.

2 Apply the chapping techniques to capture the grains and color of the peel.

3 Add the root hair, and draw the leaves with thin ink. A fresh red radish is thus finished.

TIP

It is relatively challenging to illustrate the color and grain of the peel. The key is the space between different strokes, the unpainted part.

Chinese Cabbage

The Chinese cabbage can be stored for a long time. Therefore, people in North China will buy a large quantity of Chinese cabbages in autumn to save for winter. Housewives of Korean ethnicity in Northeast China make pickles of Chinese cabbages by preserving them with dressings such as salt and hot pepper. Named "*bai cai*" (literally translated as "white vegetable") in China, the Chinese cabbage is also associated with fortune and wealth because it shares the same pronunciation with the chinese character for wealth.

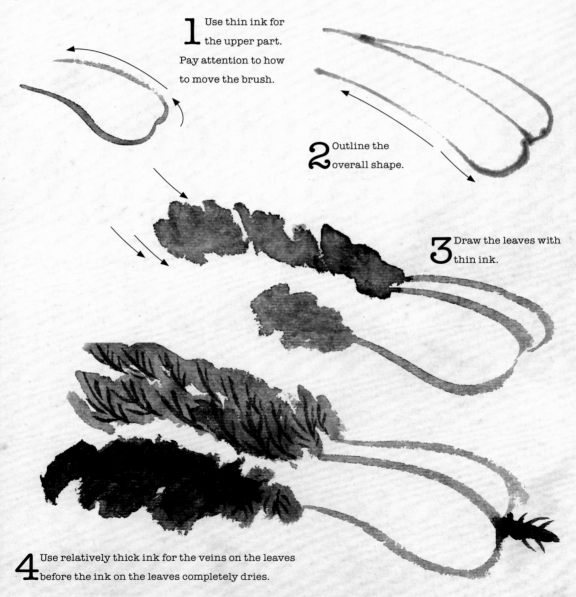

1 Use thin ink for the upper part. Pay attention to how to move the brush.

2 Outline the overall shape.

3 Draw the leaves with thin ink.

4 Use relatively thick ink for the veins on the leaves before the ink on the leaves completely dries.

Lotus Root

The lotus root is stout and knotted, hollow in the middle. It is a delicacy for the Chinese. When breaking off the lotus root by hand, you will find that the sections are still connected by the transparent thread-like strings. Therefore, the Chinese always use this phenomenon to refer to the relationship which is hard to sever, or the unchained longing between lovers.

1 Here, we will draw two sections. Start by using the thin ink for the upper section.

2 Continue with the lower section with thin ink, and use thick ink for the root hairs at the knots between the two sections. Take note that there are many pores in the cross-sections.

3 Mix the thin ink with a little ochre, and work on the surface with the chapping technique. Take note that the pores should also be colored.

Mushroom

Shiitake is uniquely found in China, and commonly known as the "delicacy of the mountain." As early as the Southern Song Dynasty, Chinese people started to cultivate shiitake. Shiitake is very easy to draw, and is thus a good option for the beginners. After learning how to draw the shiitake, we can use the same techniques to draw the *koumo* variety and white mushroom, etc.

2 Add the stalk to the cap. A shiitake is thus finished.

We can also try with those up side down.

1 When drawing the shiitake, load the brush with ochre, and draw two strokes, one on the left, the other on the right, with the end moving inward.

1 There is still a little difference concerning how to draw the *koumo* variety and shiitake. *Koumo* is white in color. Use the thin ink to outline the overall shape.

Try with other varieties.

2 Load the brush with thin ink to work on the details of the cap. Use the thick ink to add several short lines between the stalk and the cap to capture the inner composition of the cap.

Bamboo Shoot

Bamboo shoot refers to bamboos that have not broken the surface of the earth in spring. With a delicious flavor, bamboo shoots are an indispensable ingredient in Jiangnan Cuisines such as Shanghai Cuisine and Hangbang Cuisine (a dominant cuisine exclusively found in Hangzhou and its neighborhood). It is also one of the favorite subjects for Qi Baishi, the master of traditional Chinese paintings. The bamboo shoot in his paintings can always bring to life the breath of spring.

1 The peel of the bamboo shoot wrap up one layer after another, light ochre in color. When drawing the bamboo shoot, we can simply use two strokes. The right stroke is supposed to overlap a little with the left one, a little closer to the viewer than the other one.

2 Draw the overall shape of the entire bamboo shoot.

3 Use thin ink for the grain and composition of the peel. Use thick ink for the roots.

Add more bamboo shoots to make a combination.

4 Outline the grains and structure of the peel with light ink, and use thick ink for the roots.

Towel Gourd

Originally found in Indonesia, the towel gourd was introduced to China in the Song Dynasty. As one of the most common subjects in traditional Chinese painting, the towel gourd features an adorable body shape, appealing leaf shape, attractive flowers, and elegant vines. Ripe in summer, the towel gourd is usually combined together with some insects to give a breath of summer.

1 Use relatively light greenish-blue for the overall shape. The end should point upward.

2 Leave some dots in yellow, which are intended to be the withered blossoms.

3 Load the brush with thin ink and draw the grains before the color dries.

4 Use gamboge for the overall shape of the towel gourd blossoms.

5 Use fine strokes to represent the stripes on the petals. Use green for the pistils. Combine the blossoms, gourds, leaves and vines together.

Cucumber

Introduced from the Western Region (the vast area east of today's Pamirs Plateau, southeast of the Lake Balkhash and west of Gansu's Dunhuang) to China by Zhang Qian during the Western Han Dynasty on his diplomatic mission, the cucumber was originally named "*Hu* melon." Nowadays, the cucumber has become one of the most common vegetables in China. However, to use the traditional Chinese techniques to draw the cucumber will make the originally common vegetable no longer common at all.

1 Load the brush with green, and draw the overall shape within three or five strokes. Pay attention to the changes in width.

2 Use thick ink to dot on the cucumber, representing the little thorns on the surface.

3 Color the flowers with yellow. When plucked down from the vines, the flower on top is usually still blossoming.

4 Add the flowers and vines, and a cucumber painting is thus finished.

Gourd

Like the cucumber and towel gourd, the gourd also belongs to the family of vine plants. Traditional Chinese paintings generally favor the vine plants for their extensive vines and the fruits hanging on the vines. The vines and fruits always constitute an adorable scene. As one of the common subjects in traditional Chinese painting, the gourd not only features an appealing look, but is also associated with auspicious meanings.

1 Narrow in the middle, the gourd actually consists of upper and lower parts. Start with the upper one, which is narrower than the lower one.

2 Move to the lower part, which is stout in shape.

3 Apply white paint to the gourd for the highlight. Add some details such as the stalk.

4 Add the leaves and vines to produce an integral and diversified picture. We can apply the free-style technique when working on the leaves.

Pomegranate

In China, the pomegranate is associated with the auspicious meaning of prosperous offspring. In ancient China, newly-weds would hang pomegranate paintings in their room to pray for children. Besides, the pomegranate also emblematizes a good harvest. Therefore, the Chinese usually hang a pomegranate painting in their hall on festive days.

1 Load the brush with thin ink to draw the overall shape.

2 Use the thin ink and the chapping technique to capture the grains and textures of the peel. Dot on the cracks on the shell with red and yellow to represent the interior. The seeds should look crystal.

3 Use a dry brush and apply the chapping technique on the peel with light ochre to highlight the grain. Add the leaves and stalk. A pomegranate is thus finished.

We can also draw two pomegranates on one branch.

Lychee

The lychee grows south of the Qinling Mountains (the mountains extend from east to west, and traverses central China, serving as the dividing line between South and North China). It is said the Yang Yuhuan, the favorite concubine of Emperor Minghuang of Tang, loved lychee. Therefore, the emperor ordered his soldiers to transport lychees from Lingnan Region to Chang'an (today's Xi'an) within three days, exhausting a number of stout horses on the way. The emperor did all this to make his concubine smye. Therefore, the lychee is also known as the "smiling concubine."

1 Load the brush with relatively light ochre and draw a big dot.

2 Use strong ochre to add some pointed dots before the paint completely dries. Aluchee is thus finis hed.

3 In traditional Chinese painting, the lychee is generally drawn in clusters or baskets. Add some lychee leaves with relatively thick ink.

Page 92

Page 93

Page 94

Page 95

Page 97

Page 98

Page 99

Page 101

Page 102

Page 104

Page 106

Page 110

Page 111

Page 112

Page 113

Birds

Chicken

In the Chinese countryside, people often keep chickens in their yard. Generally speaking, chicken are never caged. They can run and play around the yard with no restraint. There are many techniques to paint chickens in Chinese brush painting. Here, we will focus on the suggestive style.

1 Paint an oval ink dot as the head of the chicken.

3 Use some thin ink to paint its abdomen. Then, go further to paint its beak, claws as well as its comb.

2 Add more ink dots, which are intended as its back and tail respectively.

Draw several chickens, and make them play and contest for food.

Titmouse

Titmice are very common in China. They can be seen in forests, fields and even in the proximity of farmhouses. Adopting a suggestive style to draw titmice is very simple, which is relatively easy for beginners of bird and flower paintings.

1 Draw the front view of the titmouse by using indigo to paint the titmouse's head and wing feathers.

2 Use thin ink to draw the abdomen and tail feathers.

3 Use think ink to draw the titmouse's eyes, beaks and claws, and work on the details of feathers, until a titmouse is vividly depicted.

You can also try with titmice of different kinds. Please note that the back of the titmouse, including the wings and head feathers, should be drawn in indigo, with its feathers on the abdomen and legs in thin ink, and eyes, beak, and claws in thick ink.

Hen

It is common practice to incorporate both hens and chickens in a single traditional Chinese painting to illustrate maternal love. Hens play a significant role in the life of Chinese rural communities. In ancient times, hens were kept in the yard by nearly all the households.

1 Use big red dots to draw the cockscomb and eye sockets of hens.

2 Use the ink brush to sketch the eyes, beaks and head outline.

3 Use relatively thick ink for the body, and some relatively thin ink for the transition between head and body.

An example for details of the claws.

4 Apply thicker ink to the chest, and thinner ink for the abdomen. The color in the leg is the thinnest. When drawing the tail, load the brush with thin ink and outline the tail. Use thick ink to draw the tail feathers. In the end, draw the claws in thick ink.

Cock

In the East, cocks are a symbol of martial valor. As it eats poisonous insects such as centipedes, it is sometimes considered a God driving out evil spirits.

1 Use light ink to paint the cock's chest. abdomen and legs.

2 Use thicker ink to paint its tail feather and wings, as well as its head.

3 Further elaborate on the work by adding some color at the wings to highlight its flashy features; meanwhile, load the small-headed brush with thick ink to paint some short lines on its body to exemplify the textures.

Exercise of cocks in other gestures.

Grosbeak

Grosbeaks are mostly grey-feathered. Contrasting with the dark feathers, the bright yellow beaks are striking. Actually, the beaks look waxed, glittering with luster. Therefore, they are commonly known as "*lazui*" (literally translated as the waxed-beak) in Chinese.

1 Load a fine-pointed brush with thick ink and outline the eyes and head. Please note that it has spots of white fur on both cheeks. Use thin ink to sketch the beaks, and color them with gamboge.

2 Add a little indigo to the thin ink, and paint the back feathers. Use brown for feathers on the tail and abdomen;

You can try other poses. Pay attention the basic methods to draw the head, back, abdomen, wing feathers and tail feathers.

3 Outline the abdomen with thin ink, and draw the wing feathers and tail feathers with thick ink. Paint the claws in red. A grosbeak is thus finished.

Kingfisher

Kingfishers are considered as gorgeous birds in China, because their feathers glitter with emerald, indigo luster. In the Ming and Qing Dynasties craftsmen used kingfisher feathers together with gold and silver to make jewelry. Due to its expensiveness and rarity they were exclusive accessories for female members of royal or noble families.

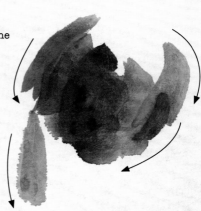

1 Use ochre for the abdomen, and blue for feathers on the back.

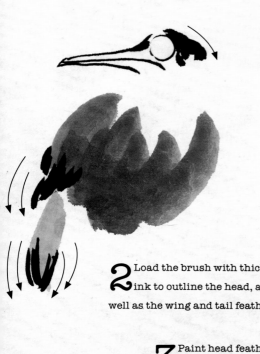

2 Load the brush with thick ink to outline the head, as well as the wing and tail feathers.

3 Paint head feathers in indigo, the same color for the back. Color the beaks in yellow, and use thick ink to draw the eyes.

TIP

The emerald blue green color on the back is supposed to be a mixture of indigo and malachite.

Magpie

It is said that the magpie is a messenger of good news, which explains why the Chinese love painting them.

1 Only ink is used to paint magpies. Use ink of different hues to draw the outline of the chest.

2 Draw the head with thicker ink.

3 Paint the tail with lighter ink, and dot on the chest and abdomen for transition. In the end, use thick ink for claws. A magpie is thus finished.

The head is relatively difficult to capture. A magpie's liveliness is expressed through its eyes.

We can also try magpies of other gestures.

Oriole

Orioles are handsome-looking with a good voice. As a recurring theme in Chinese classic poems and other forms of literature, orioles are mostly associated with beautiful spring days.

1 Draw the eyes and beaks with thick ink.

2 Apply ochre to the head feathers, and bright yellow to the abdomen feathers. Draw a few lines in a casual way to capture the texture of the feathers.

3 Use relatively dark ochre for the wings, and thick ink for wing and tail feathers. Claws should be drawn in ochre, with thick ink used for texture.

Hoopoe

Crowned with a special fan-shaped cristas, hoopoes fold them more often than display them. In an attempt to attract the opposite sex, they will unfold their breath-taking cristas, and engage in courtship by chanting the charming song.

1 Use thick ink for the head, including the beaks, eyes and crista.

2 Draw the head and back feathers with ochre.

3 Use thick ink to draw wing and tail feathers. Use thick ink to draw wing and tail feathers.

4 Use colors of low saturation, such as pink and light ochre, to work on the details of feathers on the abdomen, tail and crista. Use pink to dot the beaks.

Quail

The quail is one of the commonly consumed domesticated fowls in Chinese, just like the chick, duck and goose. Grey-feathered and ordinary-looking, the quail has no fancy tail, feather or crest. However, there is still something cute about it if we take a close observation. We should try to capture their cuteness when working on the traditional Chinese paintings.

1 What is the most special about the quail is its grey feather. Mix thin ink with a little ochre for this color.

2 Draw the feathers on the wings with thick ink. Take note that the strokes should be scattered.

3 Use thick ink for the face. Dot on the head and back.

4 Mix thin ink with ochre and further work on the back and head. Dye the abdomen, and use thick ink for the claws. Use red to dot the little tough. All these details will help to enhance the vividness.

Pigeon

The pigeon is the exemplification of peace. Legend has it that people living on the Mesopotamia Plains were the first to start domesticating the pigeon. The Egyptians had also started to keep the pigeon in the Dynasty V, while the Chinese started in the Han Dynasty. Here, we will talk about how to draw the pigeon in a suggestive way.

1 Use thick ink for the neck and the contour of chest.

2 Draw the abdomen and tail in the same way.

3 Use thin ink for the feathers on the abdomen, and thick ink for the feathers on the tail and head. Load the fine-point brush with thick ink and outline the eyes and beaks. Color them with light red. Paint the claws in the same color.

Swallow

The swallow is a small-sized bird nesting under the eaves. Their nests are made of mouthfuls of saliva and mud. People admire the industrious spirits they represent, and thus prefer to include them in the traditional Chinese paintings.

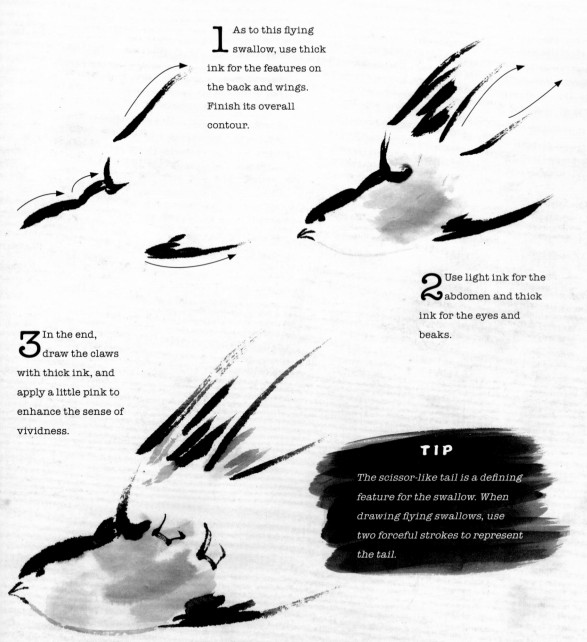

1 As to this flying swallow, use thick ink for the features on the back and wings. Finish its overall contour.

2 Use light ink for the abdomen and thick ink for the eyes and beaks.

3 In the end, draw the claws with thick ink, and apply a little pink to enhance the sense of vividness.

TIP

The scissor-like tail is a defining feature for the swallow. When drawing flying swallows, use two forceful strokes to represent the tail.

Parrot

People have special affections for parrots due to their ability to speak. Chinese also like parrots.

1 This is a green parrot. Thus, we should start to use different hues of green to paint the parrots' feathers and then paint their abdomen blue.

3 Use a brush to lengthen the lines to capture their tail feathers.

2 Use a brush to sketch out their claws, eyes, face and beaks.

TIP

Pay attention to the hooked beaks when drawing parrots. Each variety differs in terms of feather color and body shape. However, beaks are their most distinguishable feature.

There is a rich variety of parrots. Painters should observe as many different kinds as possible. It is suggested experimenting with sulphur-crested cockatoo parrots and scarlet macaws.

Take note of the different characteristics, motions and facial expressions of parrots.

Duck

There is a rich variety of duck. Generally speaking, wild ducks feature slim figures and flamboyant feathers, while domestic ducks are mostly full-figured, with white and brown feathers. When drawing ducks, pay attention to the disparities between different varieties.

1 Draw the head with thin ink, and paint the beaks and eyes with thick ink.

2 Use light pink to draw the feathers on the back and color the beaks with bright yellow.

3 Draw the remaining parts of the duck. Color the abdomen grey, while leaving certain parts uncolored. Use thick ink for the tail and wing feathers, and orange for the flippers.

White Goose

The white goose is mostly stoutly-figured. They are white-feathered and red-combed. Their bodies sway from left to right, exuding a sense of grace. In ancient Chinese poems, the white goose is a recurring theme.

1 Paint the comb and beaks with salmon.

2 Outline the head with thin ink, while taking note of the curves from the head to the neck.

3 Use thick ink to paint the eyes and outline the beaks.

4 Paint the entire body with thin ink. Add some lines following the movements of the goose to indicate the waves.

Mandarin Duck

Mandarin ducks are considered lovebirds in China, emblematizing conjugal affections, as this bird mates for life. The couple swim together, fly together and accompany each other to the end of their lives. If one of the couple dies in an unexpected way, the other will die of grief without eating or drinking.

1 Male mandarin ducks are more beautiful than the females. When drawing the former, start with the head and chest with thick ink.

2 Use ochre to draw the features on the cheek, and color the beaks with cinnabar.

3 Move to the feathers on the back, tail and wings. Pay attention to the varied color. A male mandarin duck featuring various colors is thus finished.

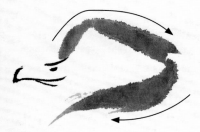

1 Male mandarin ducks are more beautiful than the females. When drawing the former, start with the head and chest with thick ink.

2 Use ochre to draw the features on the cheek, and color the beaks with cinnabar.

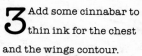

3 Add some cinnabar to thin ink for the chest and the wings contour.

4 Use some light blue for the tips of the wings, and draw the wing and tail feathers with thick ink. Draw the abdomen with light pink.

Wild Goose

As a migratory bird, wild geese fly to new destinations in a "Y-shaped" formation when seasons change. In ancient Chinese tradition, ambitious people were always compared to wild geese flying high in the sky.

1 Paint parts of the wings with thin ink.

2 Use thin ink to work further on the chest and abdomen, and relatively thick ink for the dots on the wings. Paint the wing and tail feathers with thick ink.

3 Draw the neck with thin ink, and eyes and beaks with thick ink. Pay attention to the webs on the flippers.

Try to draw a wild goose soaring to the sky.

Red-crowned Crane

Red-crowned cranes are considered auspicious birds in China and even all across Northeast China. They are the only birds that are believed to live in the celestial palace in Taoism. As emblems of longevity, red-crowned cranes appear together with pines in the paintings gifted to the elderly.

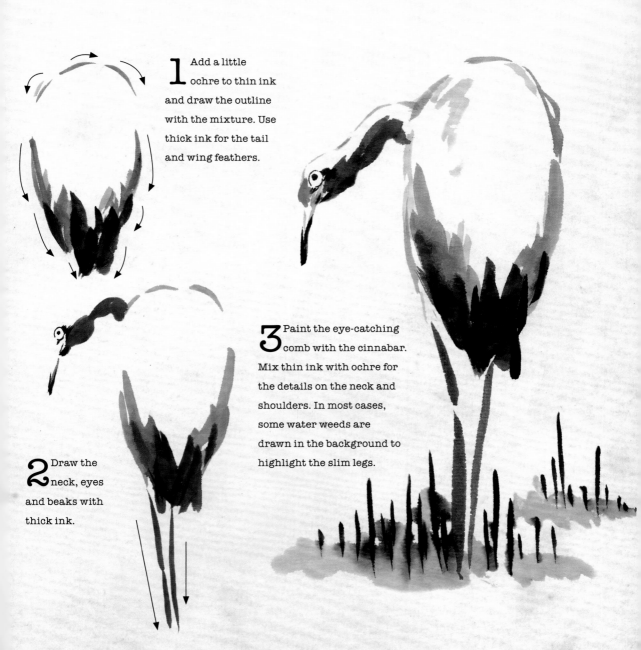

1 Add a little ochre to thin ink and draw the outline with the mixture. Use thick ink for the tail and wing feathers.

2 Draw the neck, eyes and beaks with thick ink.

3 Paint the eye-catching comb with the cinnabar. Mix thin ink with ochre for the details on the neck and shoulders. In most cases, some water weeds are drawn in the background to highlight the slim legs.

Peacocks

Known as the King of Birds, peacocks are mostly found in India, Southeast Asia, East Indies, as well as Yunnan, Guangxi and other provinces in China. Peacocks have beautiful tail feathers and plumes which are associated with wealth and auspice. Traditional Chinese painters often combine both peacocks and peonies in their paintings.

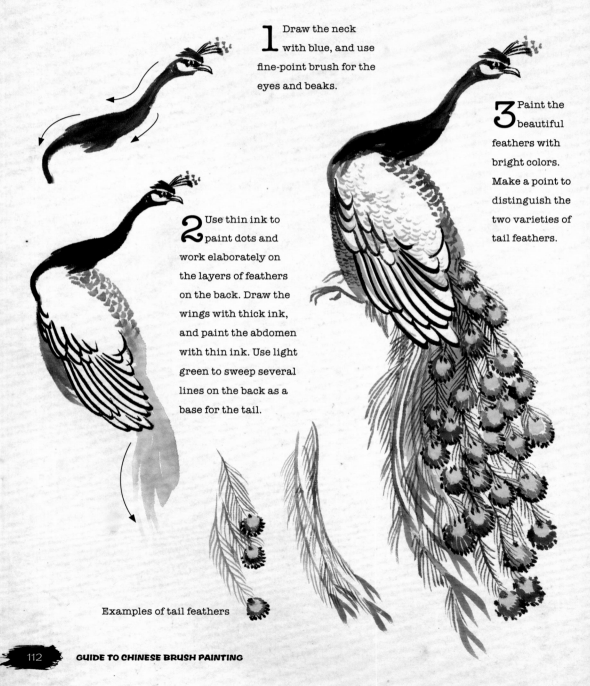

1 Draw the neck with blue, and use fine-point brush for the eyes and beaks.

2 Use thin ink to paint dots and work elaborately on the layers of feathers on the back. Draw the wings with thick ink, and paint the abdomen with thin ink. Use light green to sweep several lines on the back as a base for the tail.

3 Paint the beautiful feathers with bright colors. Make a point to distinguish the two varieties of tail feathers.

Examples of tail feathers

Golden Pheasant

Golden pheasants are believed to be amongst the most beautiful birds along with peacocks. The rarest variety is the red-abdomen golden pheasant, featuring golden comb, blue green back, orange and black dots on the chest, cinnabar abdomen, and tail feathers glittering with net black.

1 Use thick ink to sketch the head.

2 Paint the feathers on the back with thick ink. Take note that the feathers on the back are layered in a regular pattern. Use thin ink for the wings and thick ink for the wing feathers.

3 Use bright colors in the coloring stage, and then draw the long tails and the claws.

Eagle

Eagles are awe-inspiring due to their force and ferocity. They are usually compared to warriors and kings in North China and other countries in Northeast Asia. People living in Northeast China have a tradition of training eagles for hunting, which is a mysterious skill that has been passed down from generation to generation. Now, only a limited number of hunters are skilled enough to train hunting eagles.

1 Draw the the face, including eyes and beak with thick ink. Leave most parts of the eyes white to highlight the ferocity. The beaks are hooked to indicate its imposing power.

2 Use thin ink to sketch the overall shape of the head, chest and abdomen.

3 Paint the wing and tail feathers with thick ink.

Examples to draw the head: the sense of ferocity is the key.

4 Draw some dots on the back and chapped lines on the tail to illustrate the texture of the feathers. Color the beaks with bright yellow.

Fish, Shrimps and Crabs

Red Carp in Simple Strokes

Fish are a surging theme in traditional Chinese paintings. In Chinese, fish and "abundance" share the same pronunciation. Therefore, by painting fish, people are actually expressing their wish for good harvests. On Spring Festival, ancient Chinese would have fish paintings hung in the halls to pray for good harvest and a contented life.

1 Load the brush with cinnabar, and draw the body from tail to head. Start with slow movement in hand and finish with a swift action; make pauses when drawing the head; and move swiftly towards the tail. By taking note of changes in movement, the lines will be thicker in the head but thinner towards the tail.

2 Use light and swift lines to paint the fins and tail. The body generally faces outward.

3 At last, use fine-point brush to draw the lips in an elaborate way, and paint two dots for eyes, bringing a lively fish into being.

4 Add another few fish to make a group. Take note of the motions and directions. Generally speaking, arrange them in the same direction, as if they are attracted by food. Pay attention to the diversity at the same time to avoid uniformity and rigidity.

Black Carp in Simple Strokes

Ink is mostly used to draw black carp in traditional Chinese paintings. Several simplistic approaches will be introduced here. Of course, when using cinnabar, we will come up with red carp. This part is mainly concerned with the side look of black carp, different from the techniques in the former sections. Take note of the differences between the side look and overlooking perspective.

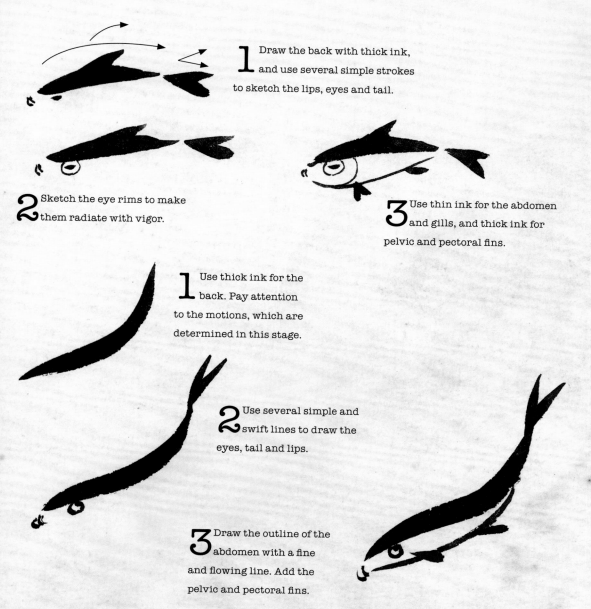

1 Draw the back with thick ink, and use several simple strokes to sketch the lips, eyes and tail.

2 Sketch the eye rims to make them radiate with vigor.

3 Use thin ink for the abdomen and gills, and thick ink for pelvic and pectoral fins.

1 Use thick ink for the back. Pay attention to the motions, which are determined in this stage.

2 Use several simple and swift lines to draw the eyes, tail and lips.

3 Draw the outline of the abdomen with a fine and flowing line. Add the pelvic and pectoral fins.

Black Carp

Black carps are commonly seen in China. Sometimes, people also use this term to refer to some unknown categories as long as they are black in color. They are relatively easy to draw, mainly used as background elements to highlight the aquatic plants. When drawing the lotuses, the painters will add several black carps to make the painting livelier.

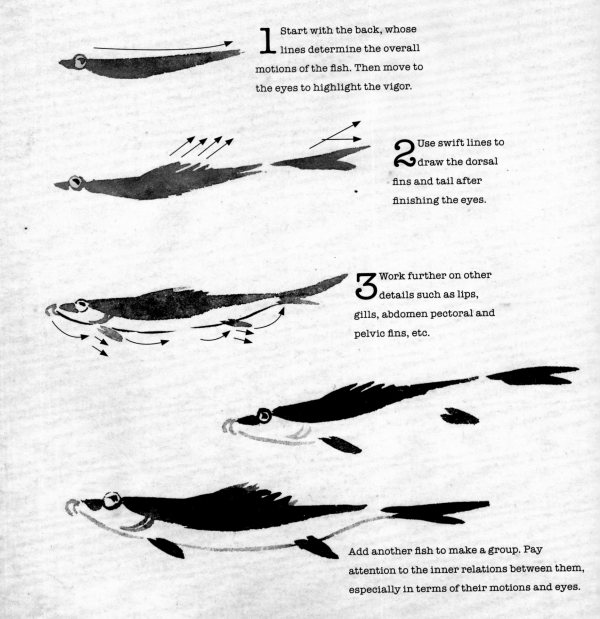

1 Start with the back, whose lines determine the overall motions of the fish. Then move to the eyes to highlight the vigor.

2 Use swift lines to draw the dorsal fins and tail after finishing the eyes.

3 Work further on other details such as lips, gills, abdomen pectoral and pelvic fins, etc.

Add another fish to make a group. Pay attention to the inner relations between them, especially in terms of their motions and eyes.

Weever

Weevers are known as one of the "Four Great Fish in China." Due to their impressive taste, weevers were a favorite topic for ancient Chinese poets, while Chinese painters also loved this kind of fish. Ferociously preying on other fish, weevers feature huge lips and rigid dorsal fins. Take note of these characteristics when drawing weevers.

1 Load a small brush with thick ink and start with the eyes. Outline the rim and then move to the half-moon-shaped pupils.

2 Stat from the eyes, and draw the outline of the head. The back is relatively dark in color. Draw the eye rims with thick ink. To illustrate the tough dorsal fins, use swift and forceful strokes. The lips also feature a darker color, which should be depicted by using fine lines in thick ink.

3 Work further on the entire body. Pay attecfion to the head, because it is relatively large in proportion. Apply thick ink to the back, which is relatively dark. The abdomen is relatively light in color, and therefore should be outlined with thin ink.

4 Add some cinnabar to gamboge. Apply the mixture to certain parts to enhance the vigor, especially onto the back. Pay attention to the alternative use of thick and thin ink to create a sense of integration.

Angel Fish

Also known as "swallow fish" and "fin fish," angel fish belongs to the category of tropical fish. Featuring lateen-shaped dorsal fins and swallow-like tails, angel fish became a favorite for Chinese after being introduced to China due to its graceful looks. There is a rich variety in terms of color, but red and black angel fish are the most common.

1 Start with the eyes by drawing an even circle along with a half-moon-shaped dot. Work further on the rims, outline the lips and sketch the dots and stripes around the eyes. The head is largely finished.

2 Use the same hue for the other parts. It is advised to move from the head to the tail, and from the back to the stomach.

3 Black angle fish are dark on the back, with lateen-shaped dorsal fins and three elongated stripes on the body. The fork in the long tail basically parallels the dorsal and pelvic fins. Take note of these defining features.

1 Use cinnabar to draw the overall shape for the back of the red angel fish in a single stroke. The perspective is the key.

2 Outline the head with thick ink. Red angel fish has smaller eyes compared with its black counterpart, and has circular stripes under the eyes.

3 Work further on the overall outline. Take note that the lines are supposed to have a smooth flow.

4 At last, use thick ink to draw the line-shaped pectoral fins. Paint the patches on the body with light ochre, and the stripes on the tail. The red hue on the back of the red angel fish is the most attractive property. Finally, it is advised to make further efforts to adjust its width.

Goldfish

The Chinese started to domesticate goldfish in the Song Dynasty over a thousand years ago.
Goldfish is actually a variation of carp. Due to careful selection and industrious effort, carp has
developed into a rich variety, including those in all colors with three-forked fish, dragon eyes,
gauze-like fins, lion-like head, bubble-like eyes and those without dorsal fins. In this part, we will
talk about how to paint dragon-eye goldfish and bubble-eye goldfish.

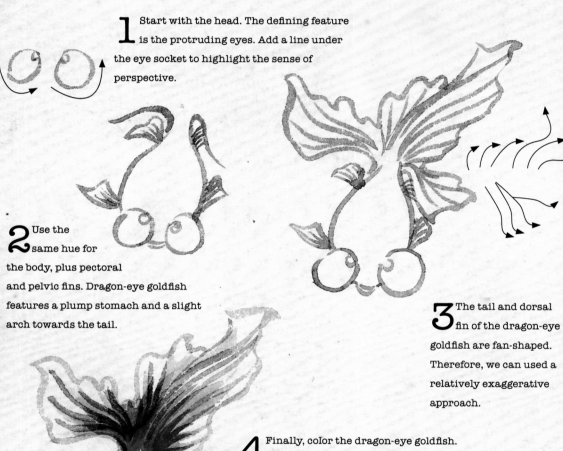

1 Start with the head. The defining feature
is the protruding eyes. Add a line under
the eye socket to highlight the sense of
perspective.

2 Use the
same hue for
the body, plus pectoral
and pelvic fins. Dragon-eye goldfish
features a plump stomach and a slight
arch towards the tail.

3 The tail and dorsal
fin of the dragon-eye
goldfish are fan-shaped.
Therefore, we can used a
relatively exaggerative
approach.

4 Finally, color the dragon-eye goldfish.
The most common category is red and
silver in color, with a red coronal, which
can be drawn with thick cinnabar. Use
relatively light cinnabar for the tips of the
tail, dorsal, pectoral, and pelvic fins.

1 When drawing the bubble-eye goldfish, start with the eyes.

2 Then move to the head and body, later to the pectoral and pelvic fins.

3 Draw the tail in a exaggerative and lively way.

4 At last, use cinnabar and thin brown for the coloring process.

Shrimp

Qi Baishi, the master of traditional Chinese painting in Modern China, is best at drawing shrimps. His shrimps are life-like, lively and full of vitality. Shrimps are mostly grey in color, but red when boiled. Generally speaking, dead creatures are rarely a theme for Chinese painters. Therefore, the shrimps in traditional Chinese paintings are mostly grey in color, with abundant vitality.

1 Use thin ink to paint the head. Load the brush with ink, and draw a relatively wide oblong. Add a line below this oblong at a certain distance away.

2 Use the same hue for the body, tail and the upper part of the head. When working on the body, make a point of the overlaps and distance between different strokes.

In traditional Chinese paintings, people are likely to draw several shrimps together to make a painting of shrimps. When working on such paintings, make it clear the overlaps between tentacles and legs.

3 Load the brush with thick ink, and draw a line in the middle of the head before the ink on the upper part dries. Following this, use a fine-point brush to draw the details such as tentacles, legs and eyes. A shrimp with threatening gestures is thus finished.

Crab

Crabs are irresistibly delicious. Chinese have a long tradition of eating crabs. Autumn is the best season to enjoy this delicacy, when the crabs are most fleshy. Therefore, in traditional Chinese paintings, chrysanthemums are always drawn together with crabs to indicate autumn.

1 Use two strokes, one left, one right, to draw the shell. The medium-sized brushes with soft fur are the best option. The ink hue is determined by the painter's personal preference.

2 Use the same hue for the eight legs and two pincers of the crabs. Pay attention to the changes and intersections. Don't make them parallel with each other. When working on the pincers use gentle strokes.

3 Use a fine-point brush to draw the eyes, tips of pincers and legs.

We can also mix some ochre or eosin, and try with different varieties by changing the color palette.

Shell

Shells of different varieties constitute a colorful collection. However, they are seldom the highlight in traditional Chinese paintings, serving only as an additional element with waterweeds to fish paintings.

1 Finish the outline of the shell.

2 Use ochre for the grain and stripes by applying the axing technique.

3 In the end, color it with yellow to enhance the texture and stripes.

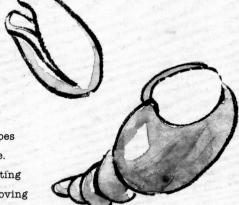

Draw shells of different shapes by using the same technique. Stick to the principle of starting with the outline and then moving to the details.

Waterweed

There is a rich variety of waterweeds. The most common categories in Chinese paintings include duckweeds, winter cherry and so on. Without roots, duckweeds float in water. Highly fragile, a slight change in water quality and wind will lead to their death. Ancient Chinese always compared travelers far away from home as duckweeds.

1 It is relatively easy to draw duckweeds. Load the brush with blackish green and draw an oblate dot.

2 Add another dot in the center when the paint is still wet. A duckweed is thus finished.

1 Use light green to draw several waterweeds.

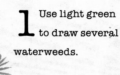

2 Use dark green on top of the light-green waterweeds.

By make a good observation of nature, and we can produce waterweeds of other varieties.

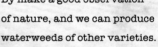

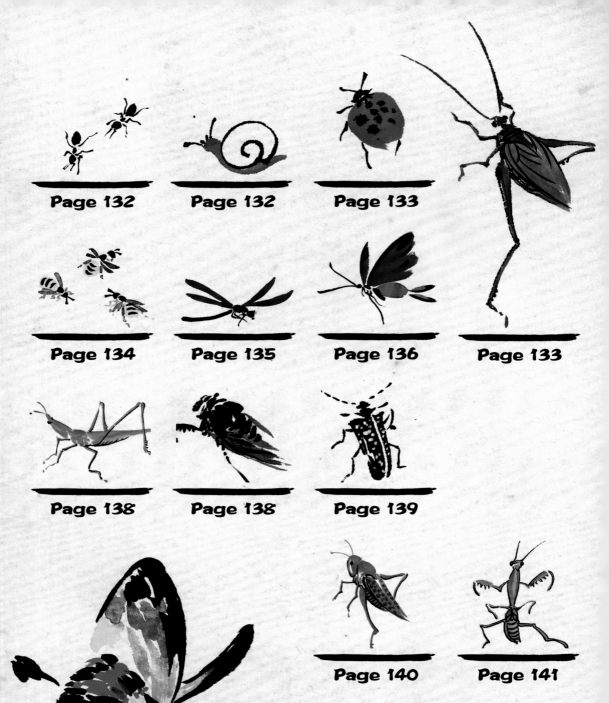

Insects

Ant

Just like the bee, the ant also works all day long, inspiring admiration for their commitment and industry. In ancient Chinese culture, the ant was also compared to insignificant figures.

1 Draw three dots with thick ink, representing the head, chest and abdomen respectively.

2 Use a fine-point brush to draw the legs with fine but twisted strokes.

3 Add two antennas, which should not be too long. An ant is thus finished.

Generally speaking, traditional Chinese paintings will not be primarily themed on a single ant. We can draw ants of different poses in the same way and make a combination.

Snail

The snail is relatively easy to draw, and is thus a good option for beginners. In traditional Chinese paintings, the snail mainly serves as a background element in bird-and-flower paintings.

1 Start with the shell. Ensure a smooth flow in the strokes.

2 Paint the body with light ochre. The snail is a member of the mollusk family; therefore we should capture this defining feature when drawing the snail.

3 In the end, load the fine-point brush with thick ink and draw the eyes and antennas. Take note that the antennas are supposed to be round-tipped.

Beetle

The beetle is categorized based on the number of black spots on its shell. Generally speaking, the beetle is drawn together with broad-leaved plants. Contrasting with the leaves, the red beetle will look striking.

 **1** Start by drawing a red round spot in two strokes, which is intended to be the shell.

 **2** Use thick ink for the legs, head and antennas.

 **3** When the ink completely dries, use thick ink to dot the shell. Seven dots make a seven-spot beetle, while five dots make a five-spot beetle.

Katydid

The katydid is noisy when eating, like a loom at work. Actually, it is a pest which feeds on the leaves of crops.

1 Mix the mineral green with a little cyaninee for the folded wings on its back.

2 Use a fine-point brush to draw the head and legs. Take note that these parts should differ from the wings in color. This difference can be realized by increasing the proportion of cyanine.

3 Use the emerald green mixture to dot the end of the wings. When the paint completely dries, load the fine-point brush with thick ink for the eyes and antennas. Work on the stripes on the back, and sketch the legs to highlight them. A katydid is thus finished.

Bee and Wasp

The bee is an exemplification of industrious spirits. Highly disciplined, they busy themselves every day to contribute to the family. In traditional Chinese paintings, the bee is often used as an adornment for the bird-and-flower paintings. When drawing peonies, we can draw one or two bees in the blossom to highlight how charmingly dedicate the flowers are.

1 Domestic bees are mostly small in size, featuring a round, relatively short and striped abdomen. Their wings are small in size, but flutter in high frequency. We should start by painting the stomach with gamboge, and the head and chest with thick ink.

2 Use relatively thin ink to draw four oval dots, which are intended as the wings.

3 At last, add the legs and antennas. Paint black stripes on the abdomen with ink before the paint completely dries.

Make careful observation of the motions of a flying bee, and paint bees of different gestures in the same way.

1 Closely related to the bee, the wasp is larger in size, featuring a relatively long, pointed brown stomach. Start by drawing the stomach with ochre, and the head and chest with thick ink.

2 Use relatively thin ink to draw four oval dots, which are intended as wings. The wings of the wasp are longer than those of the bee.

3 In the end, add the legs and antennas. Use ink to draw the black stripes on the back with ink when the paint completely dries.

Try with wasps of varied gestures by applying the same technique.

Dragonfly

The dragonfly mostly lives near water, such as pools or streams. Therefore, in traditional Chinese painting, the dragonfly is often used to adorn the aquatic plants. The lotus painting will immediately become livelier by including the dragonfly into the painting. In addition, the dragonfly can also help us to forecast the weather. When the dragonfly flies close to the water, a storm is on its way.

1 Start with the wings by using the outlining technique.

2 Load the brush with thin ink and work on the textures on the wings in a careful way.

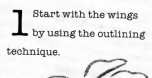

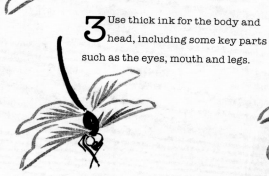

3 Use thick ink for the body and head, including some key parts such as the eyes, mouth and legs.

4 The eyes are big and protruding. Use red to dot them.

1 We can try with other methods to illustrate the wings. For example, we can use blue to paint the wings directly, finishing the four wings in four separate strokes.

2 Use thick ink for the body and head, including some key parts such as the eyes, mouth and legs.

When resting on the branches, the dragonfly will unfold its wings like a small plane, or fold them up. We can refer to the aforementioned methods to try with dragonflies in different gestures.

Butterfly

The butterfly is a beautiful creature and a symbol of unchanged love. It can help to enliven the painting. In the *Yueju* Opera, Liang Shanbo and Zhu Yingtai loved each other but were cruelly separated in life. In the end, they turn into butterflies and live happily ever after. Therefore, a single sight of the butterfly will trigger a lot of thoughts.

1 Here we will talk about how to draw the cabbage butterfly, one of the varieties commonly seen in the fields in South China. Load the brush with thin ink, and outline the two wings. Use thick ink for the two relatively large ones.

2 Use thick ink for the head, chest, abdomen, legs and the antennas.

3 Use light gamboge to dye certain parts of the wings. Use red to dot the head. A cabbage butterfly is thus finished.

1 In the passages above, we talk about how to draw the cabbage butterfly by using the outlining techniques. Here, we will try with a different approach to draw the blue-winged butterfly. First, use relatively light blue for the smaller pair of wings, and then change to deeper blue for the bigger pair.

2 When the ink completely dries, use thick ink to draw the head, chest, abdomen and then the antennas and legs. A blue-winged butterfly is thus finished.

1 The king butterfly is very colorful and complicated to draw. Load the fine-point brush with thick ink and outline the wings.

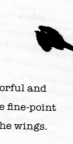

2 Draw the head, chest, abdomen, legs and antennas. Sketch the stripes on the spots on their wings.

3 Fill the spots with some bright and saturated colors such as red, yellow and blue.

Generally speaking, more than one butterfly is drawn in the traditional Chinese paintings. We can try with two or more butterflies of varied kinds to make a combination.

4 In the end, use thick ink to fill the other parts except the color spots. Work on the details, and add butterflies of different varieties to make a combination.

Grasshopper

The grasshopper has strong hind legs. We can see them hopping in the grass in summertime.

1 The grasshopper is emerald green in color. Mix the gamboge with a little cyanine and blue until we get the exact color. Use the mixture for the head, chest and abdomen.

2 Use the same hue for the legs and antennas.

3 Draw the abdomen with light ochre. When the paint completely dries, load the fine-point brush with thick ink for the details such as the eyes. A grasshopper is thus finished.

Cicada

The cicada always chirps on branches in summertime. Their sounds are loud and are one of the defining features of summer in Chinese literature.

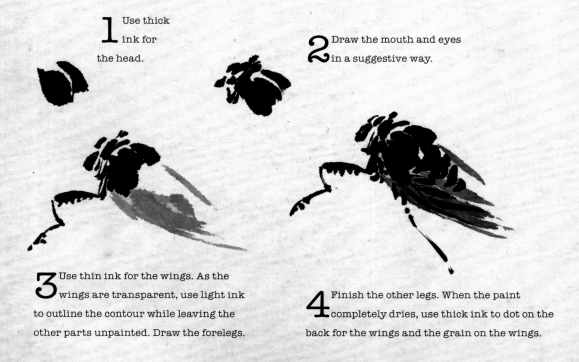

1 Use thick ink for the head.

2 Draw the mouth and eyes in a suggestive way.

3 Use thin ink for the wings. As the wings are transparent, use light ink to outline the contour while leaving the other parts unpainted. Draw the forelegs.

4 Finish the other legs. When the paint completely dries, use thick ink to dot on the back for the wings and the grain on the wings.

Longicorn

The longicorn is believed to be an insect of martial vigor. Highly recognizable, it is jet black all over, with a firm shell scattered with white spots and segmented antennas. As one of the common elements in traditional Chinese painting this kind of insect is always drawn together with flowers such as peonies and begonia to enhance a sense of vividness.

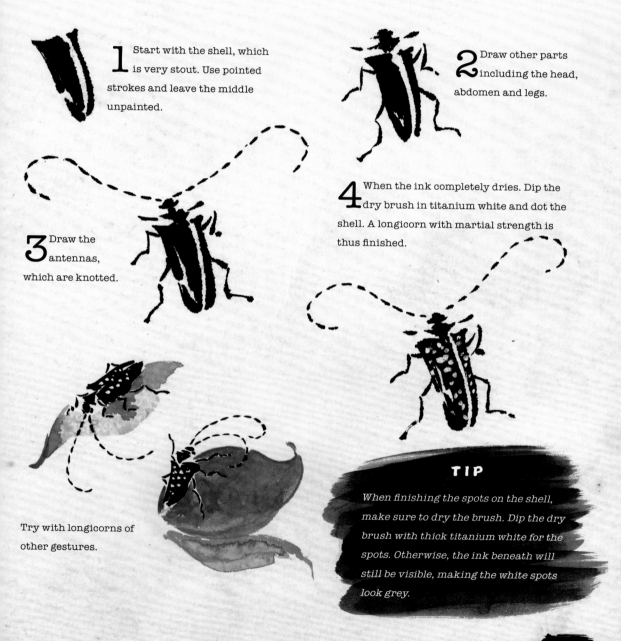

1 Start with the shell, which is very stout. Use pointed strokes and leave the middle unpainted.

2 Draw other parts including the head, abdomen and legs.

3 Draw the antennas, which are knotted.

4 When the ink completely dries. Dip the dry brush in titanium white and dot the shell. A longicorn with martial strength is thus finished.

Try with longicorns of other gestures.

TIP

When finishing the spots on the shell, make sure to dry the brush. Dip the dry brush with thick titanium white for the spots. Otherwise, the ink beneath will still be visible, making the white spots look grey.

Locust

The locust always strikes fear into the hearts of Chinese farmers. In ancient China, farming acted as a pillar industry. Feeding on crops, the locust caused great damage to farmers. In some years when locust disaster prevailed, farmers starved to death. However, the locust in the painting is not that ferocious looking. It is generally used as an adornment to flower paintings.

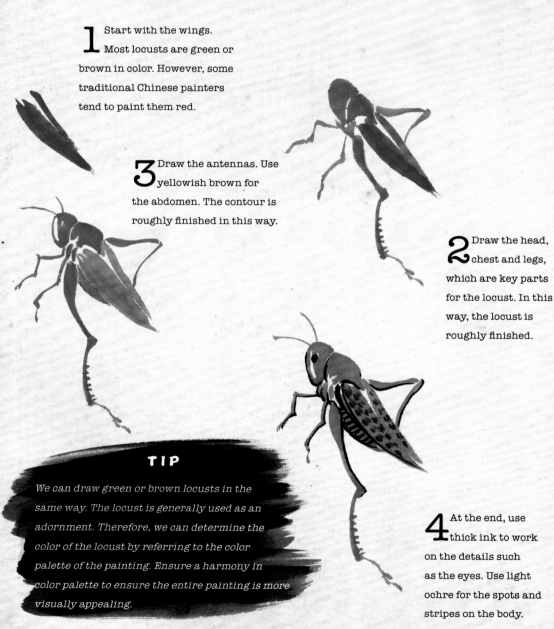

1 Start with the wings. Most locusts are green or brown in color. However, some traditional Chinese painters tend to paint them red.

3 Draw the antennas. Use yellowish brown for the abdomen. The contour is roughly finished in this way.

2 Draw the head, chest and legs, which are key parts for the locust. In this way, the locust is roughly finished.

TIP

We can draw green or brown locusts in the same way. The locust is generally used as an adornment. Therefore, we can determine the color of the locust by referring to the color palette of the painting. Ensure a harmony in color palette to ensure the entire painting is more visually appealing.

4 At the end, use thick ink to work on the details such as the eyes. Use light ochre for the spots and stripes on the body.

Mantis

To the Chinese, the mantis is a benign insect with martial vigor. With sickle-like forelegs, the mantis is good at jumping and quick to respond. It can seize a pest larger in size, and cut it into two using their forelegs. The ancient Chinese *kung fu* masters created "mantis boxing" learning from the mantis. This school of fighting is famous for its quick movements.

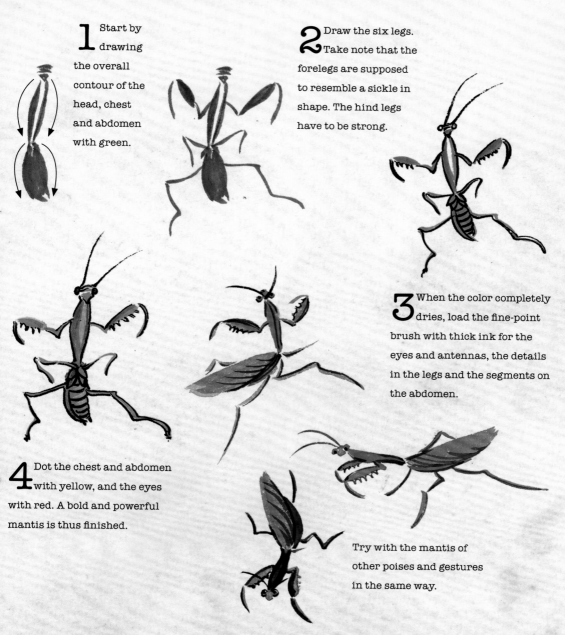

1 Start by drawing the overall contour of the head, chest and abdomen with green.

2 Draw the six legs. Take note that the forelegs are supposed to resemble a sickle in shape. The hind legs have to be strong.

3 When the color completely dries, load the fine-point brush with thick ink for the eyes and antennas, the details in the legs and the segments on the abdomen.

4 Dot the chest and abdomen with yellow, and the eyes with red. A bold and powerful mantis is thus finished.

Try with the mantis of other poises and gestures in the same way.

Page 144

Page 145

Page 146

Page 147

Page 148

Page 149

Page 150

Page 152

Page 153

Page 154

Page 155

Page 157

Page 158

Page 160

Page 161

Mammals

Dragon

Dragons do not exist in the real world. It is a combination of a snake's body, fish's scales, deer antlers, and eagle claws taken from human imagination. For thousands of years, the image of the dragons has been the emblem of the Chinese nation.

1 Traditional realistic fine-drawing techniques will be applied to draw the dragon. Load the fine-point brush with thick ink and start with the head. The dragon head is relatively complicated.

2 When working on the body, ensure a smooth movement of the brush. Start with determining the curves of its body, and then elaborate on the scales on the abdomen as well as the dorsal fins.

3 Move to other parts of the body, including the tail and claws.

Giant Panda

Widely known as the "national treasure" of China, giant pandas are born with black eye rims and plump body, charming in a naive way. When drawing pandas, capturing their naive nature is the highlight. Don't forget to add several tender bamboo shoots which are their favorite.

1 The defining feature of pandas are their black eye rims. Load the brush with thick ink and draw the eye rims, muzzle and ears.

2 Use the same hue for the black limbs. The remaining parts are mostly white in color.

Draw another panda with bamboo in its arms in the same way.

3 Use thin ink for the outline by linking up the limbs, eyes, muzzle and other parts. Add more bamboo to make the image more vivid.

Squirrel

Squirrels are lovely animals which feed on nuts such as pine cones, hazelnuts and acorns. They always eat in such a gluttonous way that their cheeks protrude out.

1 Start with the head. The squirrel is closely related to the mouse in the genetic sense. However, their eyes are larger and their ears are erect.

2 Draw the squirrel body, including the claws and legs by applying the color gradation technique featuring a free style.

3 Use a dry brush for the fluffy tail. Apply the ochre for the rims of the eyes as well as the tail.

Mouse

Mice are repulsive to most people. However, in the eyes of traditional Chinese painters, there is still something adorable about the mouse. Here, we will talk about how to draw a small mouse who wants to feed on lamp oil.

1 Load the brush with thin ink for the overall shape of the head, and use the thin ink for the eyes, nose and the whiskers.

2 Work on the body, including the feet and tail, with thin ink.

3 Apply the free-style technique to draw a lamp. Use yellow for the oil and red for the flames.

Cat

There is a famous Chinese saying, "it doesn't matter the color of the cat, so long as the cat catches the mouse." Around three thousand years ago, cats started to influence the lives of Chinese people. Helping to catch the mice, cats are good companions for people.

1 Start with the face by loading the fine-point brush to draw the eyes, the cheeks and the nose. Add more water to the ink for the ears and the black speckles on its cheeks.

2 Draw the overall shape. Take note that the cat is supposed to be flufly all over. Try to capture the textures of the furs.

3 Work on the tail and the limbs. Use different hues for the dark parts on the furs, and light ochre for the lighter parts. Color the eyes with bright yellow, and nose with red.

Dog

There are dogs of many varieties. The most common varieties in traditional Chinese paintings are the Pekingese and Shiba Inu. Foreign varieties are seldom included in the paintings. However, in the Qing Dynasty, Giuseppe Castiglione , a court painter from Italy used to apply traditional Chinese techniques to illustrate the greyhounds.

2 Then deal with the outline. Use different hues to dot the body.

1 Here we will talk about how to draw a spotty dog. First start with the head and the big ears.

3 Finish the entire body by paying attention to the gesture. When working on the spots, take note of the changes in hue and density.

TIP

When drawing such animals as cats and dogs, it is advised to make a careful observation of cats and dogs, either at home or in the neighborhood. Pay attention to their behavior and gestures to capture the vividness.

Rabbit

As a common subject in traditional Chinese paintings, rabbits feature long ears, a short tail, three-lipped mouth and red eyes. This lovely animal is always drawn together with bamboo, laurels and wormwood.

1 Start by using a fine-point brush to outline the head, including the eyes, muzzle and the long ears. Use thin ink to dye the ears.

2 Work further on the overall form and the forepaws. The rabbit features relatively short forepaws and forceful hind legs. Don't forget to work further on the rabbit head and add the whiskers.

3 Use the ink brush to draw the entire rabbit. Apply the chapping techniques to draw fur all over the body with different hues. When the ink dries, leave a tinge with light ochre. In the end, color the eyes with orange.

TIP

There are many varieties of rabbits; use different hues to draw the furs with chapping techniques. Draw the outline and leave some parts unpainted. The rabbit is thus finished. The eyes should be painted with red.

Fox

In ancient China, there is a great deal of folklore relating to the fox. In many of them, foxes transform into alluring females who seduce young male men in the mortal world. Therefore, the fox is always associated with ghosts and evil spirits in Chinese culture. In reality, the fox is a beautiful and lovable animal.

1 Start with the head. Load the brush with thick ink and draw the eyes and muzzle. Use relatively light ink for the ears. Use thin ink, the dry brush and apply the chapping techniques to capture the texture of the furs. Draw the whiskers with thick ink.

2 Use thin ink for the body, limbs and tail without outlining with thick ink. Leave a tinge with light ochre to draw a brown fox. The eyes should be drawn with orange.

Monkey

The monkey exemplifies shrewdness and agility. In China, the most common variety is the macaque. With high intelligence, the macaque is relatively close to humans. The most rare variety is the snub-nosed monkey, whose furs are as glossy as gold. Living in nearly inaccessible forest, they are difficult to approach.

1 Draw the head with a fine-point brush. Take note that the distance between ears and eyes is longer than that of humans.

2 Move to the body, including the limbs and tail.

3 Use the dry brush, thin ink and apply the chapping techniques to draw the fur. Color the cheeks and ears with red. With two fruits in arm, the monkey is snickering. Color the fruits with bright yellow after outlining them with the ink brush.

TIP

The monkey face sinks inward, while its mouth protrudes.

Red Panda

The red panda looks like the raccoon of North America. The most adorable thing about the red panda is its charming nativity. Featuring a round muzzle and round eyes, traditional Chinese painters preferred to draw the front view of the red panda. Po's *Shifu* in the film *Kungfu Panda* is actually a red panda.

1 Start with the head. Draw a square-shaped face. Pay attention to the round eyes and the white fur on the face.

2 Draw the body. The red panda is fluffy and plump in shape.

3 Paint the circular tail, and work on the details. A red panda is thus finished.

Horse

A horse can cover many miles in a single day. The Chinese always compare a talent of high potential to a "swift horse." In traditional Chinese painting, the horse is a common and favorite subject. There are many renowned horse paintings throughout history, such as Han Gan's *Herding Horses* in the Tang Dynasty, Zhao Mengfu's *Horse Herding in the Autumn Countryside* in the Yuan Dynasty, the *Galloping Horse* of the modern painting master Xu Beihong.

1 This is intended to be a galloping horse. Start with the head.

2 Draw the neck, body, buttocks and tail. Featuring beautiful muscular lines, the horse has large bulges of muscle, which is a highlight when drawing a galloping horse.

3 Paint the hooves. A galloping horse is supposed to raise his hooves in the air. An appropriately exaggerative technique can be used. Color the horse with light ochre.

Donkey

Shorter than the horse, the donkey features a rounder face, bigger eyes and longer ears. We should pay attention to the similarities and differences between the donkey and other animals such as the horse and mule. In the eyes of many people, the donkey exemplifies folly and dullness. However, in Chinese legends, many deities and hermits ride on donkeys.

1 Start with the head. Load the brush with thick ink for the overall form, including the eyes, nose and ears. Use thin ink and apply the chapping techniques for the head.

2 Move to the body. Use boorish and suggestive strokes. Use thin ink and apply the chapping techniques.

3 Draw the legs and tail. This is intended to be a donkey bowing his head and striving ahead in small steps. Ensure concerted actions.

TIP

Pay attention to the difference between the donkey and the horse. The donkey is supposed to feature a round head, big eyes, big and erect ears, shorter manes and shorter muscle tissues than the horse.

Spotted Deer

The spotted deer is a special variety in East Asia, and can be found in countries such as China, Russia and Japan. In China, the spotted deer is an animal with auspicious associations. It always appears with elderly men in traditional Chinese paintings.

1 Start with the head. Load the fine-point brush with thick ink, apply the chapping techniques and use thin ink for the outline. The most defining feature of this animal is its antlers.

3 Load the fine-point brush with thick ink to outline the legs. Color the spotted deer with ochre. Take note to leave some parts unpainted on the body, which are intended as the speckles. If we have forgot to leave elements unpainted, we can still use the titanium white to dot on the body.

2 Move to the body. Use the thin ink and chapping techniques to enhance the sense of vividness.

Sheep

Meek in nature, the sheep is covered with thick wool, which is used to produce various woolen products. Male sheep feature large horns spiral in shape, exuding a sense of mightiness. Today, there are over five hundred varieties of sheep in the world. The common varieties in China include the small-tail-fat-sheep, Xinjiang fine-wool sheep and Mongolian sheep.

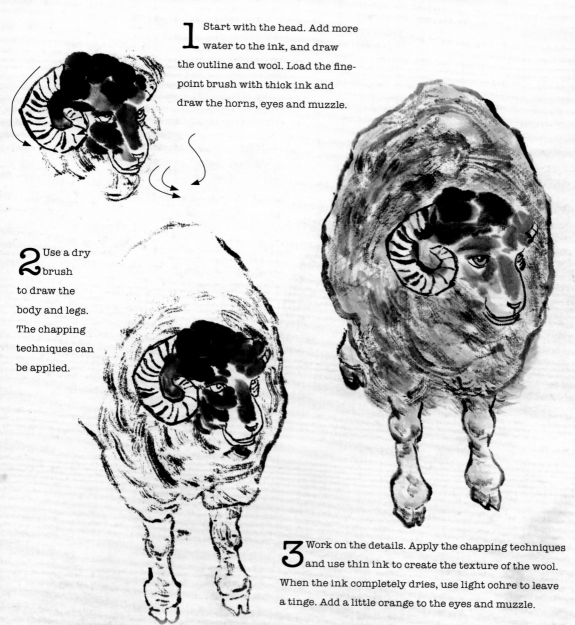

1 Start with the head. Add more water to the ink, and draw the outline and wool. Load the fine-point brush with thick ink and draw the horns, eyes and muzzle.

2 Use a dry brush to draw the body and legs. The chapping techniques can be applied.

3 Work on the details. Apply the chapping techniques and use thin ink to create the texture of the wool. When the ink completely dries, use light ochre to leave a tinge. Add a little orange to the eyes and muzzle.

Buffalo

The wild buffalo is already extinct in Chinese territory. Domesticated as a beast of burden in South China long ago, the buffalo often helps people to plough farmland. The Chinese always feel grateful, yet sorry, for the buffalo, as it toils for people in an industrious way without complaint. The Chinese usually compare committed and diligent people with a benevolent nature and sacrificial spirit to "willing buffalo."

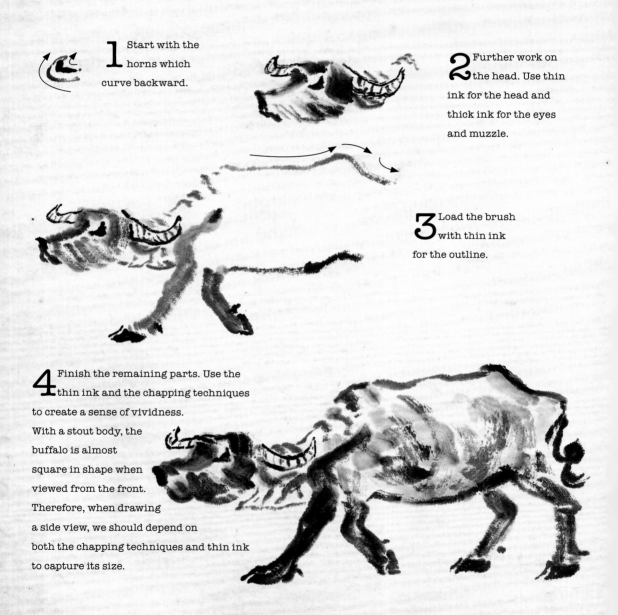

1 Start with the horns which curve backward.

2 Further work on the head. Use thin ink for the head and thick ink for the eyes and muzzle.

3 Load the brush with thin ink for the outline.

4 Finish the remaining parts. Use the thin ink and the chapping techniques to create a sense of vividness. With a stout body, the buffalo is almost square in shape when viewed from the front. Therefore, when drawing a side view, we should depend on both the chapping techniques and thin ink to capture its size.

Camel

Commonly known as the "ship of the desert," the camel can survive starvation and thirst, and travel for a long distance without eating or drinking for a span of four to five days. This is because the camel can store the nutrition and energy in its humps and water in bottle-like bubbles in the stomach. The camel has played a significant role in the establishment and prosperity of the Silk Road in ancient China as an indispensable means of transport.

2 Load the brush with thick ink and draw the neck, humps and tail.

1 Start with the head.

4 Finish the entire body, including the abdomen and the hooves. Add several strokes with thin ink to the background to capture the desert.

3 Use the light ink for the loads between the humps. The loads are usually tied to the humps.

Pig

As one of the "Five Livestock," the pig is a major source of meat for the Chinese. As early as the Neolithic Age, the Chinese started to domesticate the pig. Emblematizing silliness, nativity and folly in China, Pigsy in the classical novel *Journey to the West* exemplifies the prevailing Chinese understanding of this animal.

2 Move to the body and legs by applying the chapping technique and using thin ink.

1 Start with the head. Load the fine-point brush with thick ink, and draw the outline, the eyes and muzzle. Apply the chapping technique to capture the bulges and textures of the hide.

3 Finish the remaining parts, including the hoofs. Use pink to leave a tinge when the ink dries.

Elephant

The elephant is associated with auspicious meanings in China. In Buddhist culture, Samantabhadra Bodhisattva travels on elephant. Used to make exquisite crafts or as a remedy to diseases, ivory was highly valued. Today, due to excessive slaughter and damage to their living environment, wild Asian elephants are an endangered species.

2 Move to the body and legs. Relatively round in shape, the elephant has pillar-like stout legs, which are generally of the same thickness from top to bottom.

1 Start with the head. Load the brush with thick ink for the outline, eyes and muzzle. Don't forget the ivories.

3 Work on the details and wait until the ink dries. Use light ochre to leave a tinge on the hide to improve on the texture.

Tiger

The tiger is a synonym for the conquerors and winners in Chinese culture as an exemplification of strength and ferocity. Ancient Chinese always referred to capable and fearless generals as "tiger generals," while their descendants were known as "young tigers." As a recurring theme in traditional Chinese painting, the tiger is often drawn in a crouching gesture or captured at the second when it is about to sweep down the hill.

1 Load the brush with thick ink and draw the head. After finishing the facial organs, work on the stripes on the head.

2 Apply the same technique to draw the body. Take note of its big-size claws and the stripes on its body. Avoid intersection as the stripes are parallel.

3 Work on the details and add the tail. Color the hide with light orange. Take note that its fur is glossier than that of a lion.

Lion

As the "King of Beasts," the lion emblematizes ferocity and strength like the tiger. The lion is not a native animal in China. During the Han Dynasty, foreign envoys gifted lions to the emperor as a tribute. The emperor was impressed, believing that the lion was a divine beast from Heaven. From then on, the lion started to be closely associated with the life of Chinese people as an auspicious animal which is able to dispel evil and avoid disasters.

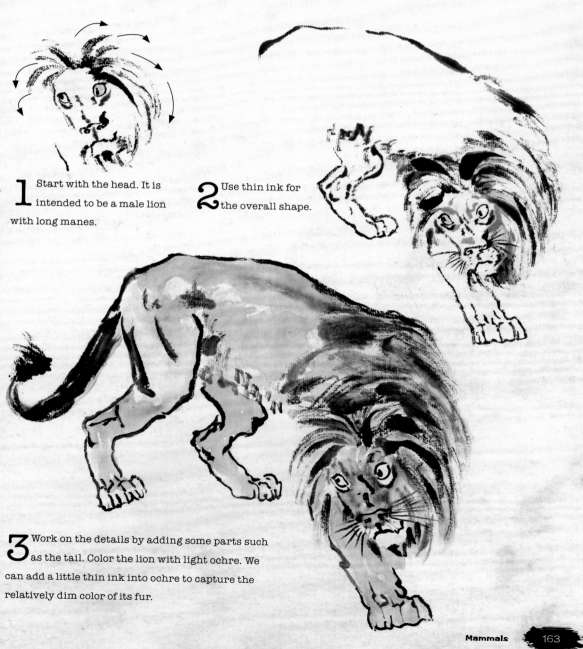

1 Start with the head. It is intended to be a male lion with long manes.

2 Use thin ink for the overall shape.

3 Work on the details by adding some parts such as the tail. Color the lion with light ochre. We can add a little thin ink into ochre to capture the relatively dim color of its fur.

Page 166

Page 167

Page 168

Page 169

Page 171

Page 172

Page 173

Page 174

Page 175

Page 176

Page 178

Page 179

Page 180

Figures

Man with Stick

In ancient Chinese landscape paintings, painters tended to include one or two figures to enhance the sense of liveliness. The mountains are both the tourists' destinations as well as the mountain inhabitants' home. All the figures included in landscape paintings are referred to as "background figures." These figures are easy to draw. The man with stick is one of the "background figures."

1 Start with the head. Use thick ink for the head and facial organs. Intended as a background figure, the eyes, nose and mouth should be roughly outlined.

2 Move to other parts such as the shoulders.

3 Use thick ink to outline the entire body. Take note that different strokes should be applied to draw the drapes on clothes and the wooden stick. When working on the drapes, the painters are supposed to shake and pause to observe the changes and directions of the drapes.

4 At last, color the figure. Actually, it is also acceptable to skip this process, as the man with stick is intended as a background figure.

Man with Hoe

The man with hoe also belongs to the category of background figures. They are generally used to adorn the farmland scenery. The man with hoe can be interpreted as common farmers. However, this kind of figure is often defined as the insightful recluse in traditional Chinese landscape paintings. They live a simple but self-sufficient life through farming practices in the countryside to escape the triviality and bustling noises of the cities.

1 Start with the head. Give him a straw hat to indicate his identity.

2 Finish the entire body. Draw a back basket and add some straw-like elements, which are intended as the harvested vegetables.

3 Color the clothes with light ochre, and dot the things in the back basket with blackish green. A mixture of ochre, yellow and orange is applied to the face.

Fisherman

The fisherman is generally intended as a "background figure" in waterscape paintings. The fisherman in ancient Chinese paintings is generally interpreted as a recluse rather than someone living on fishing. Many literati painters tended to include the recluse fisherman on the lake in their landscape paintings.

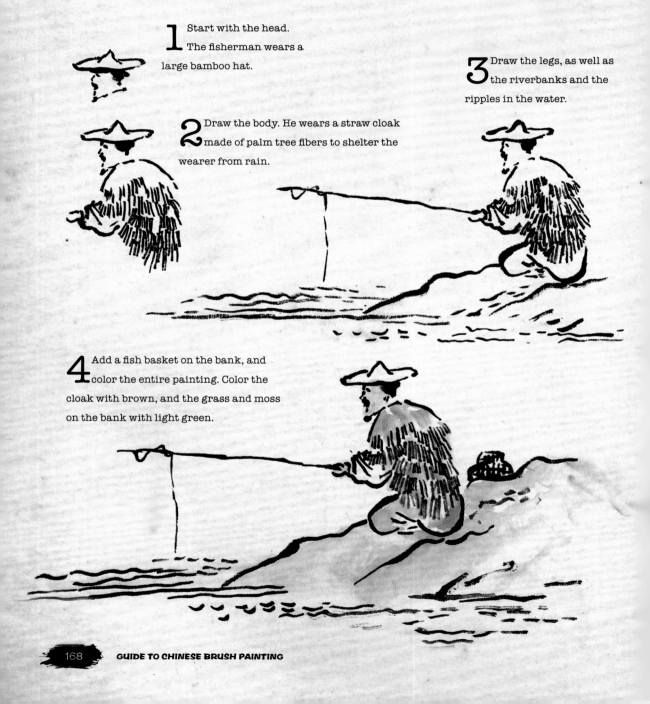

1 Start with the head. The fisherman wears a large bamboo hat.

2 Draw the body. He wears a straw cloak made of palm tree fibers to shelter the wearer from rain.

3 Draw the legs, as well as the riverbanks and the ripples in the water.

4 Add a fish basket on the bank, and color the entire painting. Color the cloak with brown, and the grass and moss on the bank with light green.

Country Gentleman

In ancient China, the peasant economy occupied a central position. The country gentleman refers to those who own farmland and possess a large quantity of wealth in a certain area, relatively cultured, virtued and respected.

1 Start with the head by using fines strokes.

2 Draw the upper body and a stick in the hand. As he does not need to labor, he has drooping sleeves.

4 Do the coloring. In order to highlight the splendor of his clothes, more than one color can be used.

3 Finish the entire body by paying attention to the intersections of the drapes on the clothes. Use the chapping techniques and thin ink on some parts to enhance the sense of vividness.

Scholar

The ancient Chinese scholar wears a long gown, a simple hair bun and beard. The scholar in this painting is supposed to bow his head and narrow his eyes, as if in deep thought. Having a prominent position in ancient China, the scholars were the elite of society. They were well educated and concerned with the fate of the country and lives of the commoners.

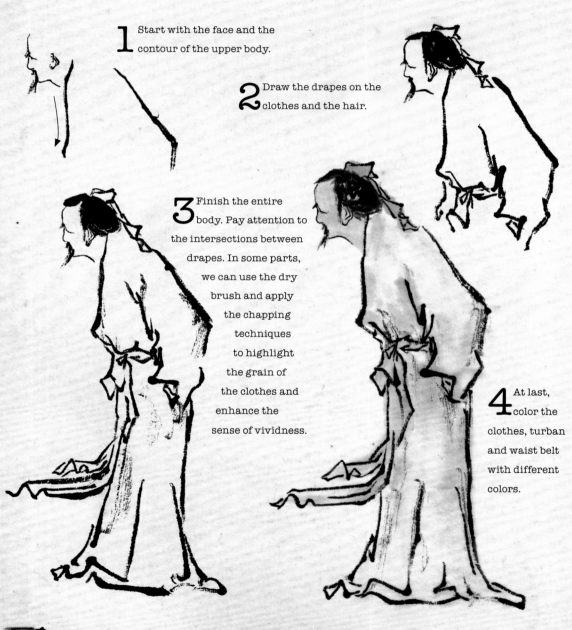

1 Start with the face and the contour of the upper body.

2 Draw the drapes on the clothes and the hair.

3 Finish the entire body. Pay attention to the intersections between drapes. In some parts, we can use the dry brush and apply the chapping techniques to highlight the grain of the clothes and enhance the sense of vividness.

4 At last, color the clothes, turban and waist belt with different colors.

Lady

"Lady portrait" is one of the most significant genres in ancient Chinese figure painting. Themed on the elegantly dressed, leisurely complexioned and well behaved lady, lady portraits of different dynasties feature varied but distinctive styles. Some are magnificent; some are gentle, while others are refreshingly graceful.

1 Start with the face and neck. Pay attention to her small mouth and arched eyebrows.

2 Draw the hair and the upper body. When drawing females, use fine strokes.

3 Further work on the body. Take note of the drifting sleeves and ribbons.

4 Finish the coloring process. Color the clothes with a relatively bright color.

Poet

Poems occupy a prominent position in the domain of ancient Chinese literature. Generally speaking, the poets were more respected than composers and novelists. The poet in this painting looks into the sky with one hand behind his back and the other extended, as if offering over his musings on life.

1 Start with the head and apply the chapping technique.

2 Work on the contour of the shoulders.

3 Draw the details such as the chest, stomach, waist, arms and hands. Pay attention to drapes on the clothes. Outlining with thick ink and chapping with thin ink are jointly used here.

4 After finishing the entire body, color the poet by mixing the ochre with a little red paint.

The Elderly

In ancient China, it is commonly believed that aged people with rosy cheeks and long moustaches and eyebrows carry an air of deity. Painters prefer this kind of aged person, believing that they exude a special aura. When working on the elderly, pay attention to the drooping corners of eyes and the evident nasolabial folds. Both are defining features for the elderly.

1 Start with the head by outlining with a relatively fine brush.

3 Finish the entire body. This aged man sits with folded legs. Color him with pink and orange.

2 Draw the upper body. His back is arched due to senior age.

TIP

Aged females and males share similarities in terms of facial characteristics. Remove the moustache and eyebrow, and add the hair.

Arhat

There is a distinctive genre in ancient Chinese painting. Commonly known as "religious painting," this genre is mainly themed on the Buddhist or Taoist practitioners. The arhat is a Buddhist category.

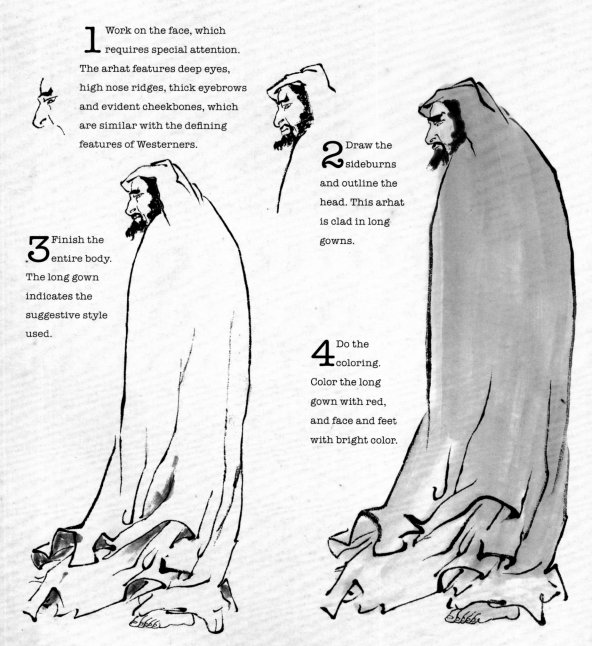

1 Work on the face, which requires special attention. The arhat features deep eyes, high nose ridges, thick eyebrows and evident cheekbones, which are similar with the defining features of Westerners.

2 Draw the sideburns and outline the head. This arhat is clad in long gowns.

3 Finish the entire body. The long gown indicates the suggestive style used.

4 Do the coloring. Color the long gown with red, and face and feet with bright color.

Zhong Kui

Zhong Kui is a deity in ancient Chinese legends. He is a favorite of the Chinese because he can intimidate evil spirits. With a distinctive look, this legendary figure features a leopard's head, circular eyes, ironic face, and intertwining sideburns. Stoutly built, he looks ferocious and tough. He usually wears a crimson gown, and a judge's cap, holding a sword in hand.

1 Start with the head. Pay attention to the big, round eyes. The face should look vivid.

2 Draw the sideburns. Though thick, they still observe a certain pattern.

3 Finish the entire body. His bare arms are covered with hair. Zhong Kui is one of the most challenging figures in traditional Chinese paintings.

4 Color the clothes with bright red.

Go Player

When we have to include more than one figure in the painting, we have to capture the defining features of every figure in a proper way, while paying attention to the interactions between different figures. The interactions between different figures are mainly reflected in the exchanges in action and eyes. We can start with a pair of go players when studying paintings featuring multiple figures.

1 Start with the go player facing the front. Draw the head first. This player wears a turban and beard.

2 Continue to finish the entire body. This player arches his back, with stones in hand and an absorbed look on the face.

3 Then move to the one with his back to the viewers. Start with the head and outline of the back.

4 Continue to finish the entire body. The player sits on the ground, putting all his weight on his hand.

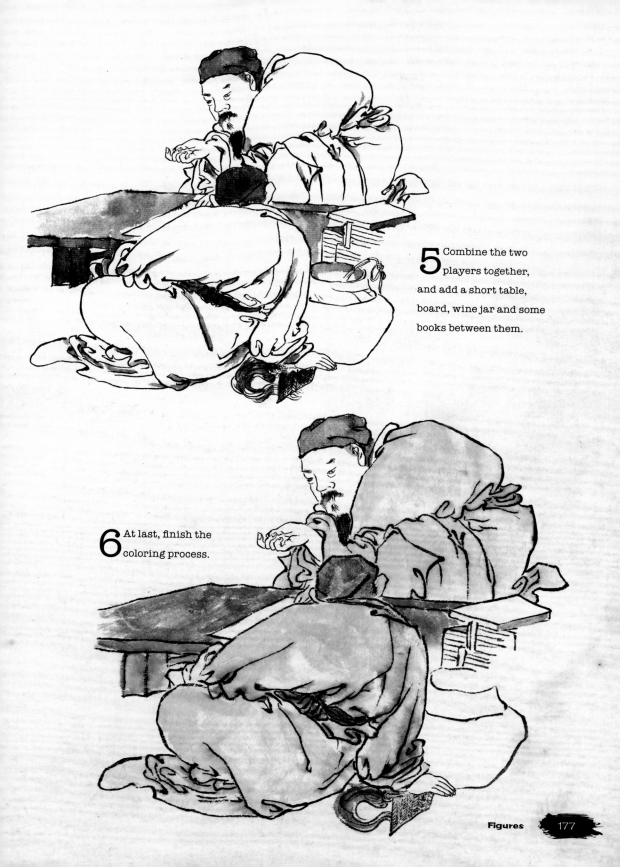

5 Combine the two players together, and add a short table, board, wine jar and some books between them.

6 At last, finish the coloring process.

Tibetan Woman

As a multi-ethnic country, China has fifty-six ethnic groups, including the Han. As early as the Southern and Northern Dynasties, painters started to include ethnic people in their paintings, such as the *Tribute Bearers to the Court*. In modern times, more and more painters have chosen ethnic groups as subjects. The Tibetans are mainly concentrated in the Tibet Autonomous Religion as well as other provinces such as Qinghai, Yunnan and Sichuan. The Tibetan clothes are highly distinctive.

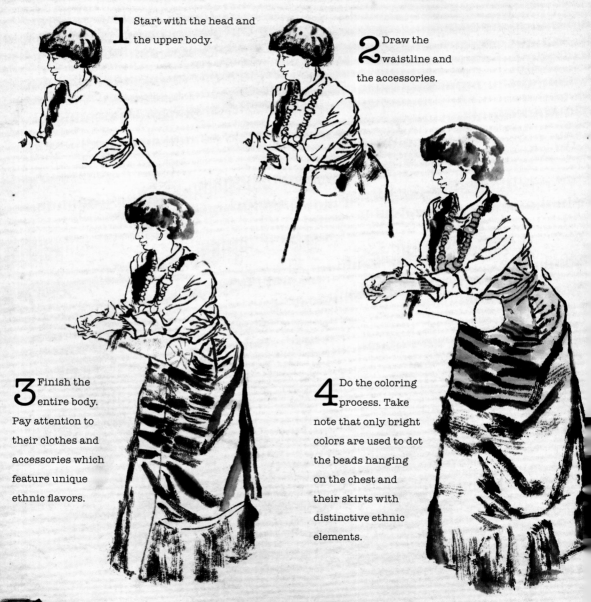

1 Start with the head and the upper body.

2 Draw the waistline and the accessories.

3 Finish the entire body. Pay attention to their clothes and accessories which feature unique ethnic flavors.

4 Do the coloring process. Take note that only bright colors are used to dot the beads hanging on the chest and their skirts with distinctive ethnic elements.

Korean Woman

The Korean ethnic groups are mainly concentrated in Northeast China (including Liaoning, Jilin and Heilongjiang) and are outstanding singers and dancers. Korean women like cladding themselves in long skirts featuring high waistlines and wide drapes, and wearing a hair bun. Here, we will draw a Korean woman dancing while playing the drum.

1 Start with the head and arms by taking note of the motions of their flying sleeves.

2 Use the ink brush to draw the drum on the chest and hands to beat the drum.

3 Work on the long skirt with bright red. Dot on the cuffs and collar with a little red and green. A painting of Korean dance flowing with dynamics is thus finished.

Little Girl

The little girl is a recurring subject in traditional Chinese paintings. In ancient China, it was a common practice to draw plump babies to wish for prosperous offspring. In the modern times, the paintings tend to focus on the nativity and naughtiness of children. The little girl in the painting is lying on the ground, reading a book in a preoccupied way.

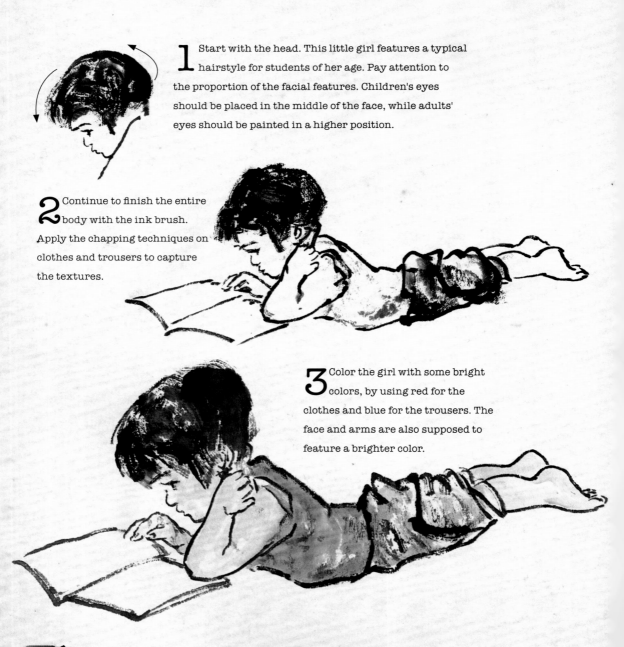

1 Start with the head. This little girl features a typical hairstyle for students of her age. Pay attention to the proportion of the facial features. Children's eyes should be placed in the middle of the face, while adults' eyes should be painted in a higher position.

2 Continue to finish the entire body with the ink brush. Apply the chapping techniques on clothes and trousers to capture the textures.

3 Color the girl with some bright colors, by using red for the clothes and blue for the trousers. The face and arms are also supposed to feature a brighter color.

Little Boy

When drawing little boys, the highlight is to capture his naughtiness. This little body rests his head on his arms, and sits cross-legged, just like an adult. He seems to be resting, or thinking about where to have fun. When drawing little boys, we usually color their clothes with bright colors to add a sense of liveliness to the picture.

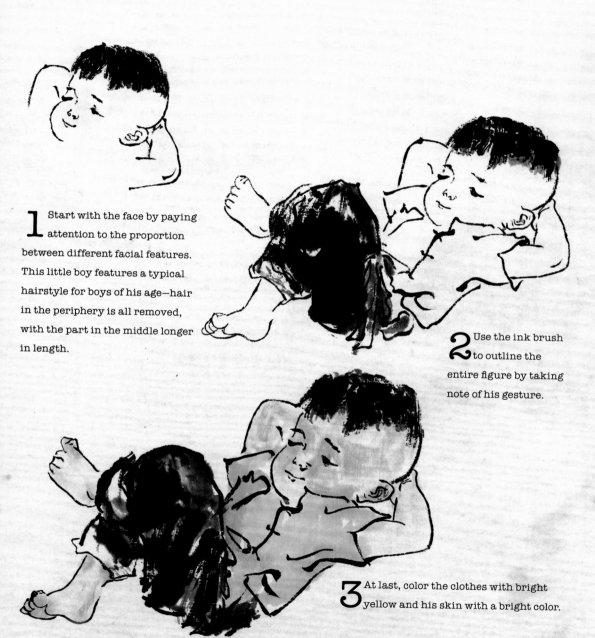

1 Start with the face by paying attention to the proportion between different facial features. This little boy features a typical hairstyle for boys of his age—hair in the periphery is all removed, with the part in the middle longer in length.

2 Use the ink brush to outline the entire figure by taking note of his gesture.

3 At last, color the clothes with bright yellow and his skin with a bright color.

Maid

When drawing maids who are supposed to be twelve or thirteen years old, we should take full considerations of their distinctive features. Unlike girls five or six years old, their faces are longer, and the eyes are positioned higher. Here, we will talk about how to draw a beautiful maid with a basket in one hand and skirt hemline in the other hand.

1 Start with the head. Load the fine brush with thick ink, and draw the hair by using the chapping techniques.

2 Use the ink brush to outline the clothes. Pay attention to the changes in the drapes.

TIP

Generally speaking, we are supposed to do the coloring when the ink completely dries.

3 Draw the feet and legs. Use a dry brush and apply the chapping techniques in certain parts to enhance the sense of vividness. When drawing maids, take note of the head-body ratio. Generally speaking, a maid of twelve or thirteen years old is supposed to feature a head-body ratio of 1:5.

4 It finally comes to the coloring process. The maid wears a red skirt, which is quite eye-catching. Generally speaking, we should start the coloring process when the ink completely dries. After the coloring process, use the ink brush to work on the details, such as the eyes and the floral patterns on the skirt.

Page 192

Page 193

Page 198

Page 199

Landscape

Pine

As one of the common subjects in landscape painting, pine is loved by the Chinese for its lofty virtues and varied shapes. Its trunk and branches, though stout, are not straight but twisting. When drawing the pine, the key is to highlight that the tree must have survived many disadvantageous weather conditions.

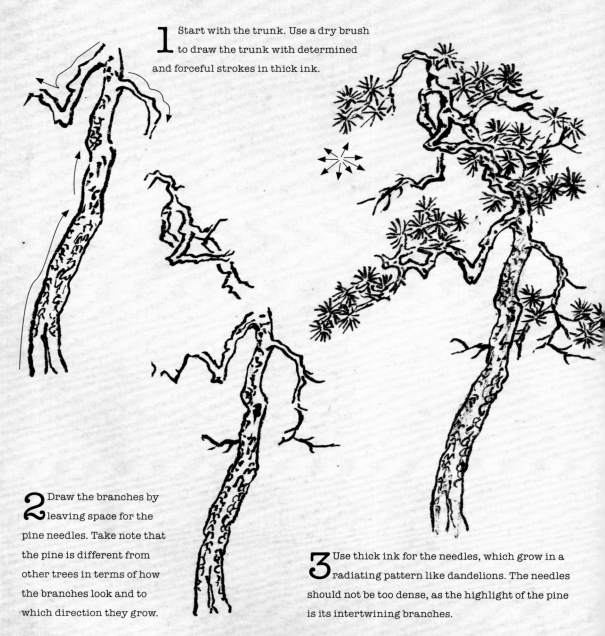

1 Start with the trunk. Use a dry brush to draw the trunk with determined and forceful strokes in thick ink.

2 Draw the branches by leaving space for the pine needles. Take note that the pine is different from other trees in terms of how the branches look and to which direction they grow.

3 Use thick ink for the needles, which grow in a radiating pattern like dandelions. The needles should not be too dense, as the highlight of the pine is its intertwining branches.

4 In the end, use light ochre to color the trunk before the ink dries. Use blackish green to color the needles.

After grasping the basic techniques to draw the pine, we can try with pines of other poises. The most significant but challenging part is how to capture the trunk and branches.

Phoenix Tree

The phoenix tree represents lofty and admirable virtues. There is a saying in ancient China "plant the phoenix trees to attract the phoenix," as it was believed that phoenix only perched on this kind of tree. Therefore, it was a common practice to plant the phoenix tree before or behind the residence in hope for the arrival of phoenix and good luck. The phoenix tree belongs to the family of broad-leaved trees.

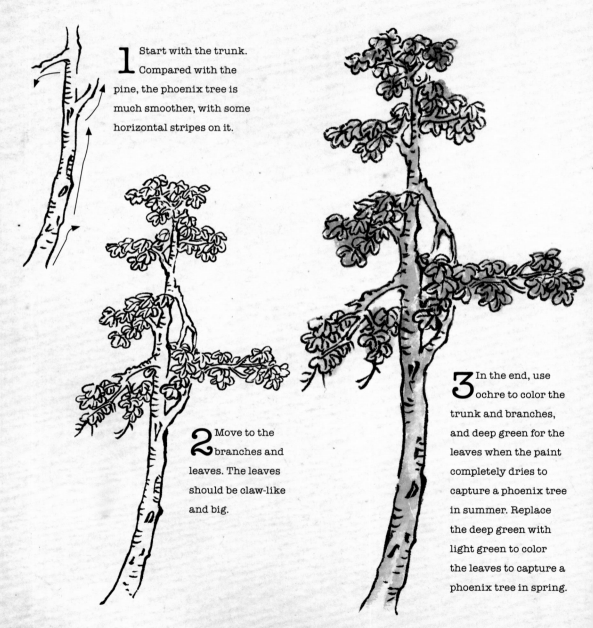

1 Start with the trunk. Compared with the pine, the phoenix tree is much smoother, with some horizontal stripes on it.

2 Move to the branches and leaves. The leaves should be claw-like and big.

3 In the end, use ochre to color the trunk and branches, and deep green for the leaves when the paint completely dries to capture a phoenix tree in summer. Replace the deep green with light green to color the leaves to capture a phoenix tree in spring.

Willow

Willow is a recurring theme both in landscape paintings and ancient Chinese poems. Sharing the same pronunciation with the Chinese character "to stay," the willow is often used to express the wish to persuade family or friends to stay longer. In the landscape painting, the willow is always combined with riverbanks. The willow branches gently kissing the water surface is believed to be one of the most enchanting scenes.

1 First start with the trunk and branches. The trunk tilts horizontally.

2 Move to the branches, long and bendy.

3 Use green to color the surroundings of the branches to represent the leaves. Generally speaking, the trees in landscape painting are positioned far from the viewer. Therefore, there is no need to draw the leaves piece by piece. A blurry contour is enough.

Tree Combination

In landscape paintings, it is a common practice to combine different varieties of trees together. The ragged contour will construct an appealing scene. We will show to the readers what effects will be produced by combining different varieties of trees together. When drawing tree combinations, we need to take considerations of seasonal factors and climate conditions. For example, drawing a desolate pagoda tree in winter together with a flourishing willow in summer will look absurd.

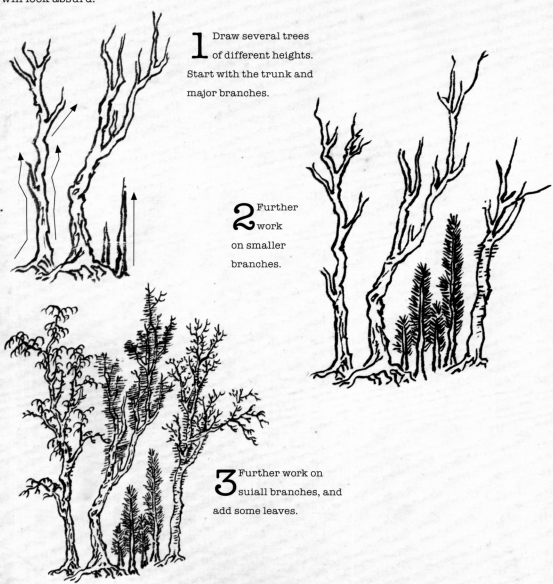

1 Draw several trees of different heights. Start with the trunk and major branches.

2 Further work on smaller branches.

3 Further work on suiall branches, and add some leaves.

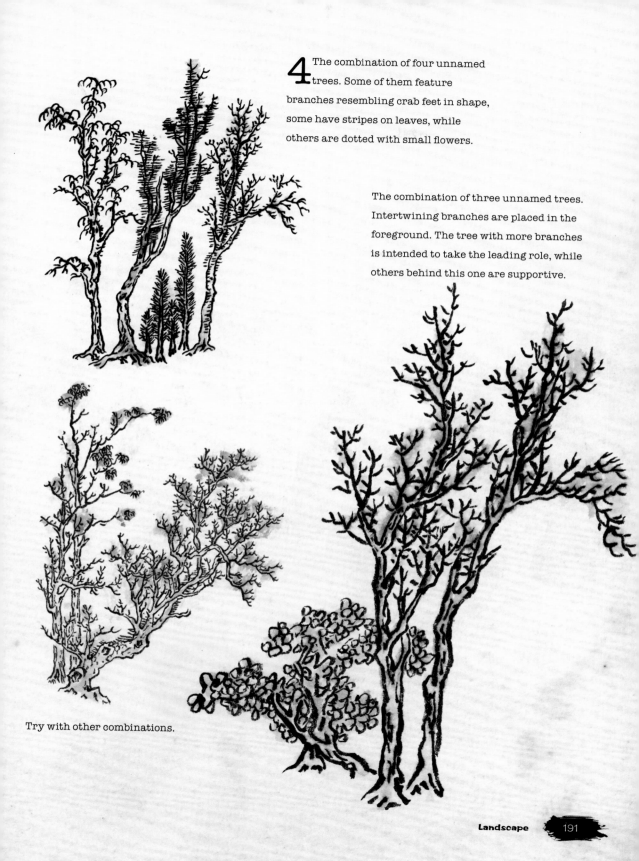

4 The combination of four unnamed trees. Some of them feature branches resembling crab feet in shape, some have stripes on leaves, while others are dotted with small flowers.

The combination of three unnamed trees. Intertwining branches are placed in the foreground. The tree with more branches is intended to take the leading role, while others behind this one are supportive.

Try with other combinations.

Pagoda Tree

The pagoda tree is very common in North China. In many cities such as Beijing and Xi'an, the streets are lined with pagoda trees. In landscape paintings, the so-called dragon-clawed pagoda tree is preferred to create a desolate ambience. Its small leaves flourish in summer but wither in winter.

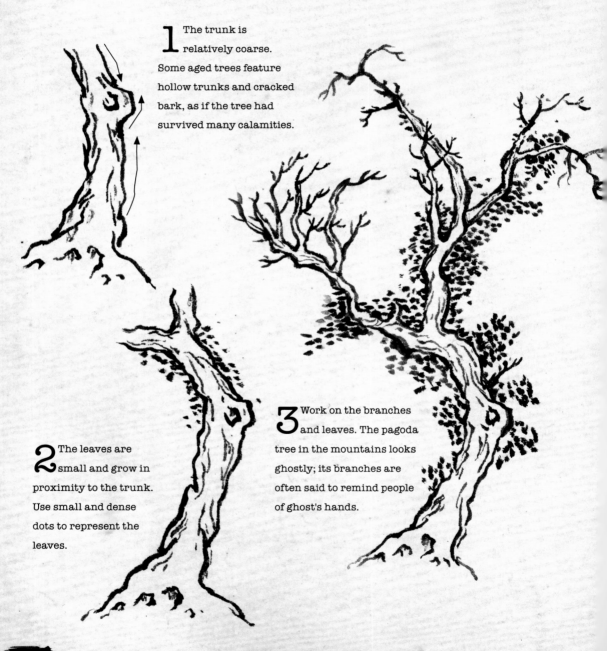

1 The trunk is relatively coarse. Some aged trees feature hollow trunks and cracked bark, as if the tree had survived many calamities.

2 The leaves are small and grow in proximity to the trunk. Use small and dense dots to represent the leaves.

3 Work on the branches and leaves. The pagoda tree in the mountains looks ghostly; its branches are often said to remind people of ghost's hands.

Reed

In the waterscape painting, we often draw reeds on the riverbank for decoration. The reeds grow in clusters. Therefore, we have to pay attention to the overlaps and intersections when drawing reeds. On the riverside, a carpet of reeds dance in the wind, exuding a poetic touch.

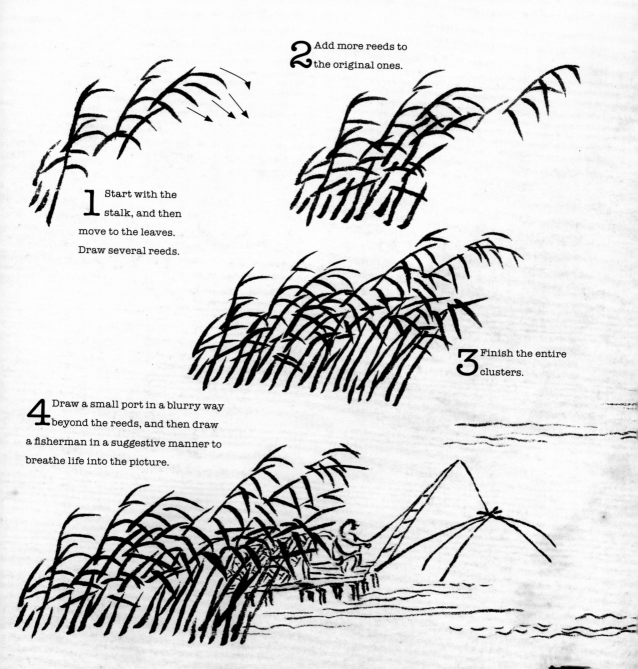

2 Add more reeds to the original ones.

1 Start with the stalk, and then move to the leaves. Draw several reeds.

3 Finish the entire clusters.

4 Draw a small port in a blurry way beyond the reeds, and then draw a fisherman in a suggestive manner to breathe life into the picture.

Fence

Fences are one of the most common elements in landscape paintings. It is common practice to paint a household living in deep mountains. Before the residence are always some fences made of bamboo, wood or clay. When drawing the fence, it is advised to apply a free style. Avoid rigidity and regularity.

1 Here, we will talk about how to draw a relatively complicated bamboo fence. Start with the structure.

2 Such fences are always built on a supporting structure, consisting of intertwining bamboo strips. Load a fine brush with thick ink and work on the grains of the fences. The gate is supposed to consist of bamboo strips woven in a regular pattern.

Try another kind of bamboo fence in the same way. This variety is relatively simple, featuring regularly-patterned bamboo strips. We can also add one or two trees behind the fence to enhance the sense of vividness.

The clay fence (a short wall in the strict sense) is relatively easy to draw. Sitting on a stone base, the clay is capped with straw to avoid rain damage.

Bridge

In classic Chinese landscape paintings as well as those featuring pavilions and towers as the highlight (such as the ruler painting), the bridge is an indispensable adornment. The bridge can be as simple as the single-plank bridge or as complicated as the stone arch bridge. Here, we will talk about several techniques to draw the bridge. When working on landscape paintings, we can select appropriate bridge as adornments based on the overall atmosphere of the picture.

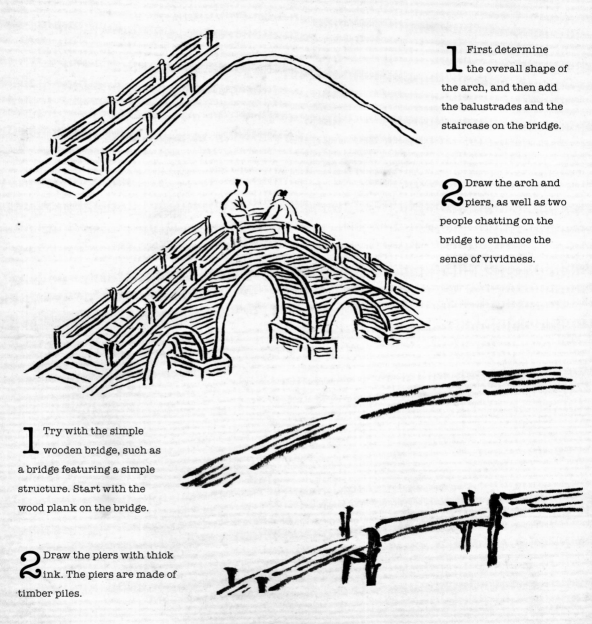

1 First determine the overall shape of the arch, and then add the balustrades and the staircase on the bridge.

2 Draw the arch and piers, as well as two people chatting on the bridge to enhance the sense of vividness.

1 Try with the simple wooden bridge, such as a bridge featuring a simple structure. Start with the wood plank on the bridge.

2 Draw the piers with thick ink. The piers are made of timber piles.

Work on the slopes on the side of the bridge. Dot the slopes with trees, and add ripples beneath the bridge. Add two walking people on the bridge. A painting of bridge in rain is thus finished.

1 Start with the bridge floor when drawing the stone bridge.

2 Load the fine brush with thick ink and determine the position of the piers, which are supposed to be made of timber piles.

3 Draw all the piers. The stone bridge is thus finished.

Pavilion

The pavilion is a distinctive architectural form in China. Solely supported by columns rather than walls, the pavilion opens directly to four directions, and features a sense of spaciousness. The pavilion is primarily intended to provide a place for rest and relaxation. In ancient China, a well-developed transportation network was not in place. Therefore, pavilions were erected along the courier route every five kilometers so that travelers can take repose along the way. Later, this architectural form was reproduced in the courtyards of the emperor, nobles and scholars.

1 Start with the roof, which is supposed to be square in shape.

2 Further work on the roof.

3 After finishing the roof, add four columns. The pavilion is roughly finished. Add two people at rest in the pavilion to enhance the sense of vividness.

TIP

The highlight of the pavilion is the roof. We can try with hexagonal pavilion and octagonal pavilion in the same way.

Boat

In Chinese landscape paintings, mountains and rivers are supposed to go hand in hand. Waterscape is an indispensable element in landscape paintings. Imagine how vivid the entire painting will look with a small boat drifting in the lake and stream. In landscape paintings, especially those with the waterscape as the highlight, the boat is a great adornment.

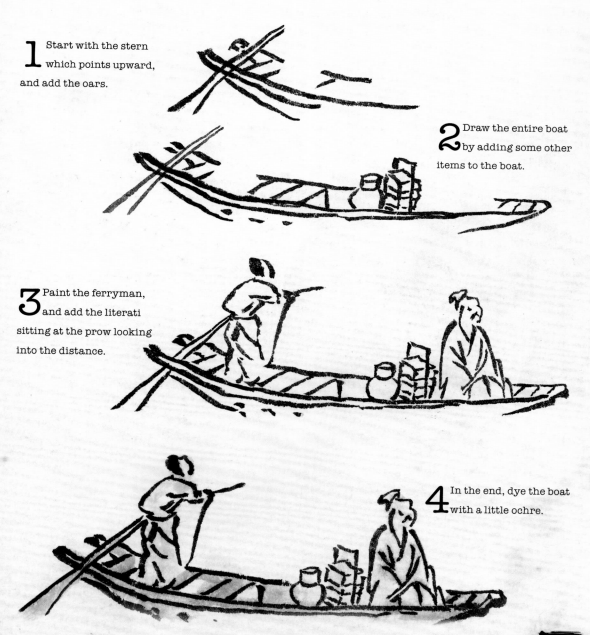

1 Start with the stern which points upward, and add the oars.

2 Draw the entire boat by adding some other items to the boat.

3 Paint the ferryman, and add the literati sitting at the prow looking into the distance.

4 In the end, dye the boat with a little ochre.

Farmhouse

In ancient China, farmhouses were generally quite ramshackle. Some are walled with wood plants, some are thatched, while others are fenced with bamboo strips. However, these farmhouses featuring a crude style exemplified solitude. Traditional Chinese painters prefer to include a farmhouse in the landscape paintings to express their wish to live a reclusive life.

1 Start with the basic structure. Determine the positions of the fence, central hall and the wing room. Draw the roof.

2 Work on the details, such as the texture of the bamboo fence, the door and window, and so on. When drawing the farmhouse, pay attention to the perspective. The door of the farmhouse is wide open so that the viewers can see what is inside the central hall.

Thatched Cottage

The thatched cottage is roofed with straw, featuring a crude and primitive touch. Easy to draw, it symbolizes a sense of seclusion. Therefore, it is usually employed to match natural scenery. When working on the thatched cottage, the painters are supposed to use simple and crude strokes. There is no need to detail the door and windows.

1 Start with the overall structure of the roof.

2 Draw some tilted lines to represent the straw and highlight the texture.

3 Use the ink brush to work on the details such as the door, window and columns.

4 Color the thatched cottage with light ochre.

Two-story Tower

In the genre paintings, towers of two stories and multiple stories are frequently shown in landscape paintings. In ancient China, folk residences were no higher than three stories. When painting the two-storied tower, take note of the contrast between the tall and short towers. Use the roof of the short towers to highlight the towering one.

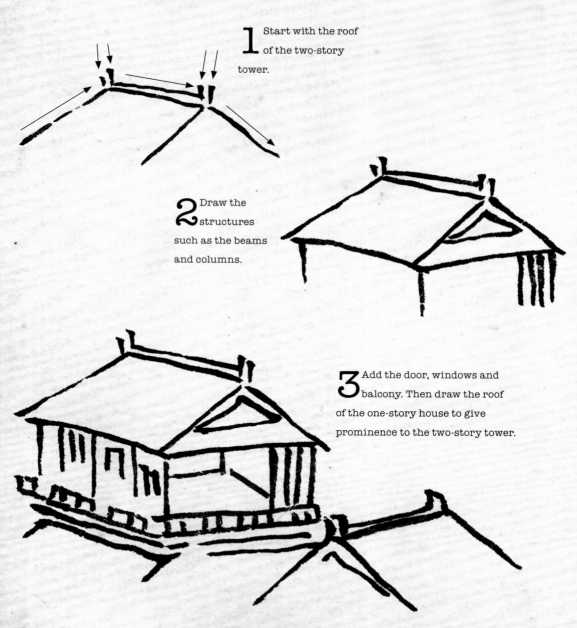

1 Start with the roof of the two-story tower.

2 Draw the structures such as the beams and columns.

3 Add the door, windows and balcony. Then draw the roof of the one-story house to give prominence to the two-story tower.

Tiled House

In ancient China, folk residences are mostly roofed with tiles and supported by wooden beams and columns. When the wooden structure was finished, tiles produced in furnaces would be attached to the roof. Sheltering the residents from wind and rain, the tiled house is very airy.

1 Start with the overall structure as well as the details such as the door, window, columns and beams.

2 Add the tiles, which are supposed to be laid layer after layer in a regular pattern. Start by drawing some parallel strokes on the roof and add small arcs between the parallel lines. The tiled house is thus finished, exuding a sense of vividness.

Grand Tower

Here we will talk about how to draw a relatively grander tower. The extent of grandeur is determined by the complicatedness of some key components such as the roof, overhanging eaves, corridor and arch. The most complex component of the tower we are drawing is the roof. We should have a profound understanding of the structural relationship.

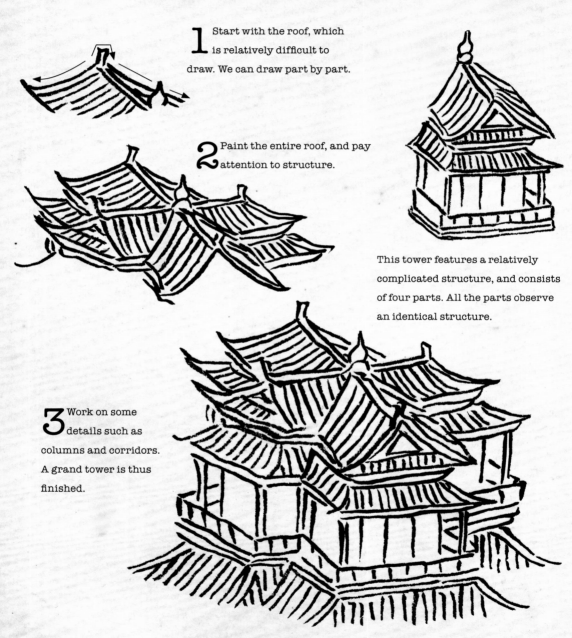

1 Start with the roof, which is relatively difficult to draw. We can draw part by part.

2 Paint the entire roof, and pay attention to structure.

This tower features a relatively complicated structure, and consists of four parts. All the parts observe an identical structure.

3 Work on some details such as columns and corridors. A grand tower is thus finished.

Temple

The temple is intended to enshrine the Buddha. Some temples were constructed on high mountains, and others were built in bustling cities. Some renowned and ancient temples are large in size, and incorporate a complex of towering pavilions. In temple paintings, the gate, main shrine, Buddhist pagoda, and scripture hall are indispensable architectural elements.

1 Start with the roof of the main shrine, where the Buddha is worshipped. This building features the largest area and the most splendid roof.

2 Work further on the double-eaved roof. Add details such as the door and windows.

3 Add components such as the gate, Buddhist pagoda and scripture halls. An ancient temple is thus finished.

Waves

Water is an indispensable element in landscape painting. Many painters are interested in capturing various forms of the water. Ma Yuan, a renowned Southern Song landscape painter, produced a collection of paintings to capture the beauty of rivers, lakes and the sea. Under the influence of varied air currents and wind directions, waters will exhibit different characteristics. Here we will talk about how to draw the surging waves.

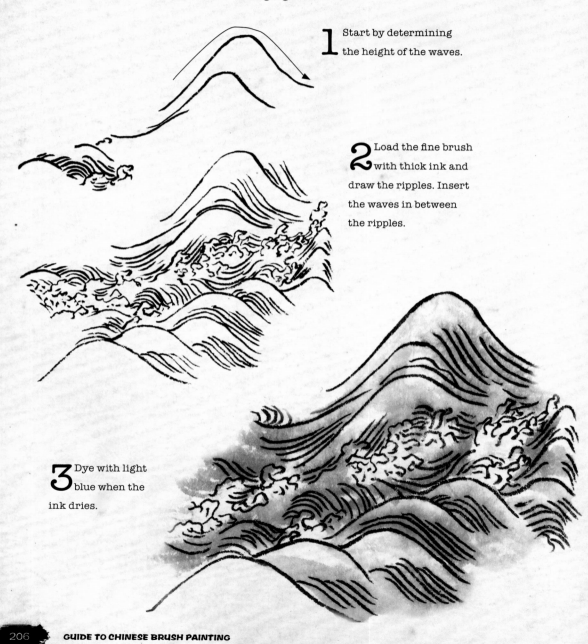

1 Start by determining the height of the waves.

2 Load the fine brush with thick ink and draw the ripples. Insert the waves in between the ripples.

3 Dye with light blue when the ink dries.

Riverbank

In landscape paintings, waterside scenery is the highlight. There are many varieties of riverbank. Some are gentle, some are cliffy, some are craggy, and others are weedy. Here, we will talk about how to draw the riverbanks featuring both water and rocks, as well as a little moss and grass. The waters are gentle and dotted with waterweeds.

2 Add the rocks, mud, moss and grass.

1 First determine the basic composition of the riverbank.

3 Further work on the details, and draw the ripples in the distance.

Craggy-topped Hill

In landscape paintings, the most challenging, dynamic and glamorous element is the hilly rock. We have to make good use of the chapping techniques to capture the charisma of the hilly rocks. There is a rich variety of chapping techniques, which are categorized into many different kinds in terms of their characteristics and forms, such as bull-hair chapping and ax-chapping methods. Here, we will talk about how to draw a craggy-topped hill.

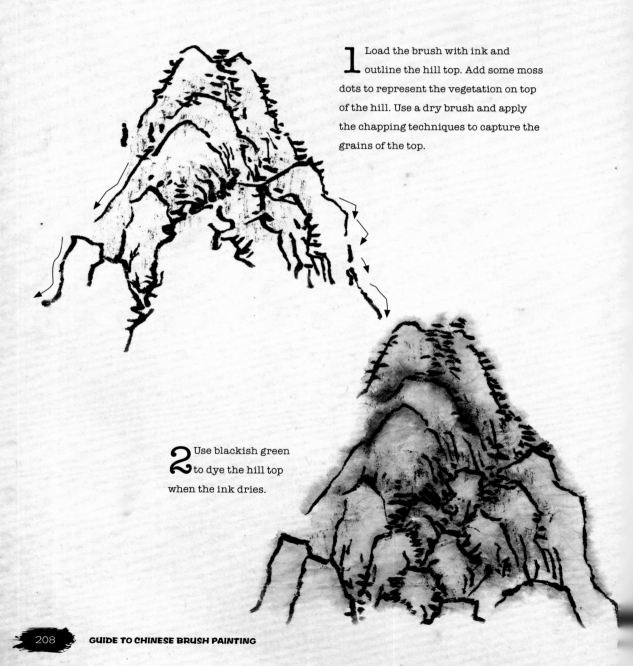

1 Load the brush with ink and outline the hill top. Add some moss dots to represent the vegetation on top of the hill. Use a dry brush and apply the chapping techniques to capture the grains of the top.

2 Use blackish green to dye the hill top when the ink dries.

Big-topped Hill

When illustrating the towering mountains, painters always focus on the sense of weight to make the mountain visually imposing. When working on such mountains, pay attention to the movement of the strokes and direction of the mountains. Mountains capped with flourishing vegetation can be dyed with green paint, while bald hills can be dyed with ochre.

1 Load the brush with ink, and outline the hill.

2 Dot on the mountain to represent the vegetation.

3 Use a dry brush to capture the hill with the chapping techniques and further work on the details.

4 Dye the hill with ochre when the ink dries.

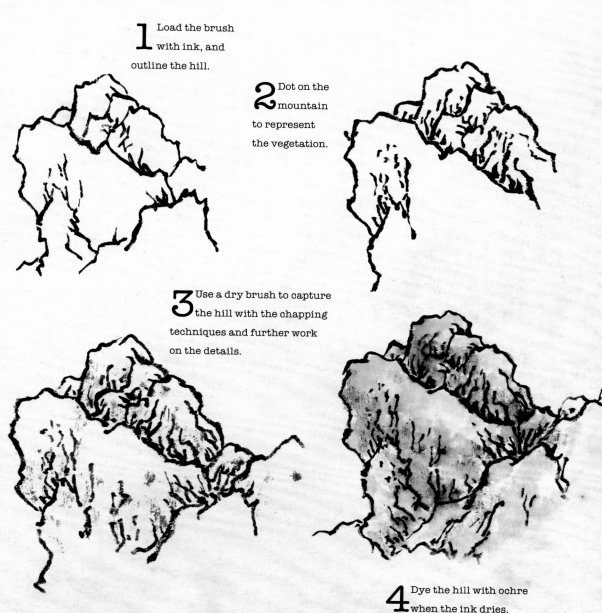

Flat-topped Hill

Traditional Chinese painters prefer precipitous mountains. Some terrace-shaped mountains with flat tops often appear in landscape paintings. When drawing such mountains, take note of the contrast between the horizontal and vertical sections to highlight how towering the hill is. Traditional Chinese painters prefer precipitous mountains. Some terrace-shaped mountains with flat tops often appear in landscape paintings.

1 This is a flat-topped hill. Start with the top, which is a flat surface.

2 Continue to draw the hill by using the chapping and outlining techniques.

3 Color the hill with light ochre.

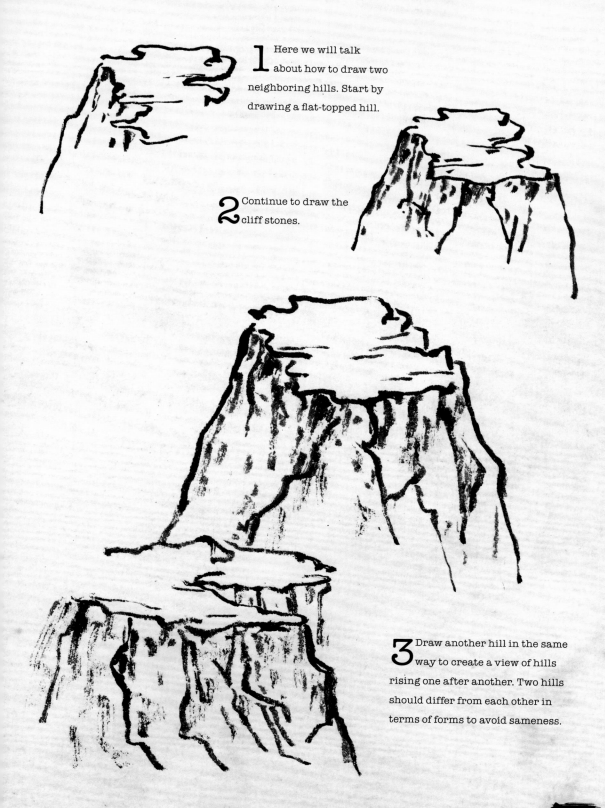

1 Here we will talk about how to draw two neighboring hills. Start by drawing a flat-topped hill.

2 Continue to draw the cliff stones.

3 Draw another hill in the same way to create a view of hills rising one after another. Two hills should differ from each other in terms of forms to avoid sameness.

Falls

We have to incorporate a lot of key techniques and elements in landscape paintings, including the chapping techniques, moss-dotting techniques, as well as those applied to draw mountain, rock, waters and vegetation. Lushan Falls in Jiangxi Province are a big favorite to the literati. Li Bai, a renowned poet of the Tang Dynasty compared it to the galaxy, while Shen Zhou, a master of painting in the Ming Dynasty, reproduced the scene in Li Bai's poem in his painting *Lofty Lushan*.

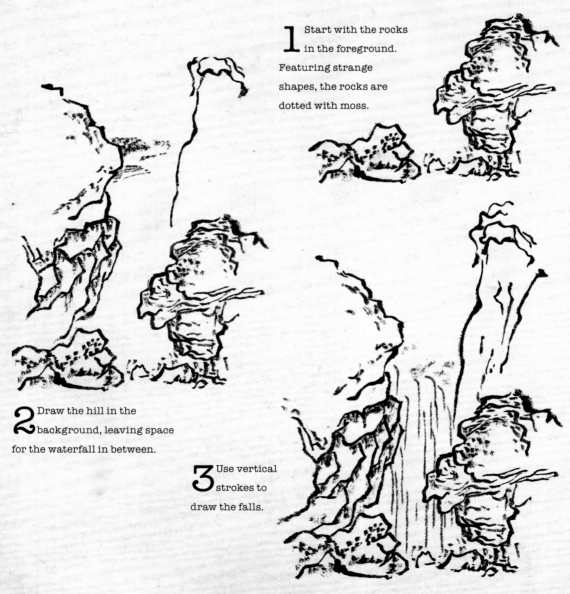

1 Start with the rocks in the foreground. Featuring strange shapes, the rocks are dotted with moss.

2 Draw the hill in the background, leaving space for the waterfall in between.

3 Use vertical strokes to draw the falls.

4 Use blackish green to dye the rock and hill. Pay attention to the changes in hue.

Try with other varieties of falls in the same way. The falls can be of different heights and widths. Generally speaking, rocks around wider falls are supposed to be shorter to highlight the splendor of the falls, while the falls in deep valleys or on towering mountains should be long and thin to capture the dynamics of the swift torrents.

GALLERY

Dragonflies Playing in the Lotus

The lotus is a defining feature of the summertime. When drawing the lotus, we can add two dragonflies playing in the lotuses. If the painting still seems empty, we can add several fish swimming through the waterweeds.

Dragonfly: As to the two dragonflies in the painting, one is blue in color, the other green; one rests on the leaves, the other flying towards the pistils. The diversity has created an interesting contrast and interaction.

Please refer to Page 135

Lotus: Draw the stalk and leaves in the suggestive style while using the outlining techniques for the petals. Use ga mboge for the center of the flowers and leave the other parts uncolored.

Please refer to Pages 34 & 35

Composition: This painting features a relatively complicated composition. The highlight is the pair of dragonflies and the lotus. When working on the painting, start by determining the positions for the highlights, and then add some secondary elements such as the stalk and swimming fish. In this way, we can avoid disorder.

Fish: Use thin ink for the swimming fish, and add several baby black carp in a suggestive way.

Please refer to Pages 188 & 119

Wild Geese and the Reed

The reed and the wild goose will make an optimal combination. The wild goose tends to rest itself in a watery place on their migration to the South. Therefore, they can always be spotted amid the reeds. When working on the painting featuring the wild goose and the reed, we should blur the goose in a certain way to produce a meaningful atmosphere.

Reed: Paint several reeds to represent a large cluster.

Please refer to Page 39

Geese: One goose is taking a rest, while the other is combing its feathers, creating a contrast between the dynamic and the static.

Please refer to Page 110

Riverbank: Both the reed and the wild geese are commonly found near water. Add the slopes in the distance to enhance the sense of depth.

Please refer to Page 207

Composition: This painting has observed the "corner approach," one of the most common techniques in traditional Chinese paintings. Subjects such as the reed and wild goose are all arranged in the lower right corner, while the upper left corner is empty. This approach is employed to create a diversification in density.

Painting of Flowers

We can come up with a colorful flower painting by combining flowers of different varieties together. When working on such paintings, take considerations of the seasonal factors. We will end up as a joke if we include the winter plum blossoms and the autumn chrysanthemums together. In addition, we should take serious thought of the harmony in the color palette. The beauty of flower painting is that by putting various flowers together, we can make flowers of different colors complement each other and add radiance to each other. We can also include some insects into the painting of different flowers to enhance the sense of vividness.

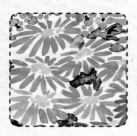

Calliopsis: Put the calliopsis in the foreground.

Please refer to Page 54

Bee: The bee helps to enhance the sense of vividness in the painting.

Please refer to Page 134

Flower-de-luce: Place it in the medium shot.

Please refer to Page 42

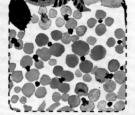

Hydrangea: It can fill in the gaps between the calliopsis and flower-de-luce.

Please refer to Page 47

Camellia: The camellia is supposed to work as an adornment.

Please refer to Page 57

Composition: The highlight is placed somewhere a little right to the middle. First establish a triangular structure which is stable and dynamic by using flowers of different varieties, heights and poises for overlaps and intersections.

A Basket of Cherries

In the former chapters, we have talked about how to draw a cherry. A cherry is not enough to make a painting, but a basket of cherries can be. Draw a basket full of cherries and add other summer fruits such as a peach, apricot, plum, lychee and so on. A painting to capture a breath of early summer is thus finished.

Cherry: When drawing a number of cherries, pay attention to the changes in density.

Please refer to Page 66

Peach: Draw two peaches in the basket. Different from the cherry, the presence of peaches actually adds to the sense of diversity in the painting.

Please refer to Page 70

Composition: The traditional Chinese paintings value a harmonized integration between the "concentrated" and the "scattered." This basketful of cherries represents the "concentrated," while several cherries outside the basket stand for the "scattered." An integration of both "the concentrated" and "the scattered" will enhance the sense of vividness.

Basket: When drawing the basket, it is advised to use a dry brush to illustrate the texture of the basket.

TIP

We can also add some common insects in the summer, such as snails, grasshoppers, locusts and so on. These lovely insects add to the sense of vividness of the painting.

A Basket of Vegetables

Different people prefer different vegetables. In this painting, the basket is full of various vegetables, including Chinese cabbages, radishes, eggplants and so on. The mushroom, shallot and garlic stay out of the basket. It seems that these fresh vegetables will turn into delicious cuisine in a second. The Chinese usually include various vegetables in the same painting to exemplify the good harvest and abundant life.

Chinese cabbage: The Chinese cabbage plays a leading role.

Please refer to Page 81

Basket: Draw the basket with a lighter color to match with the vegetables in color.

Radish: Its beautiful color is the highlight of this painting.

Please refer to Page 80

Shallot & Garlic: They are placed outside the basket to represent the "scattering" elements.

Please refer to Pages 56 & 58

Eggplant: Purple eggplants show themselves from the cracks in the basket.

Please refer to Page 72

Green Pepper: Green peppers and purple eggplants create a harmonized combination.

Please refer to Page 94

Composition: Take note of the contrast between the "concentrated" and "scattering" elements. This painting shares similarities with the one featuring a basket of cherries.

Fish Swimming in Aquatic Plants

Sharing the same pronunciation with "abundance" in China, the fish is a common subject in traditional Chinese painting due to its association with the wish for a wealthy life. In this painting, two weevers are intended as the protagonists, with several small black carps playing a supportive role. Add some aquatic plants as adornments. A painting featuring fish and aquatic plants is thus finished. We can use light green and light blue to dye in order to capture the special properties of water and enhance the sense of vividness.

Weever: The two weevers are the protagonists in the painting, and are supposed to be drawn bigger.

Please refer to Page 121

Small Black Carp: Small black carps live in groups. Take note that they should swim in the same direction.

Please refer to Page 118

Aquatic Plant: Add some aquatic plants for adornment.

Please refer to Page 129

Composition: The perspective approach in traditional Chinese paintings is varied from that observed in western paintings. The former is mostly based on cavalier perspective instead of focus perspective. In this painting featuring both fish and aquatic plants, the cavalier perspective is employed.

Cat and Butterflies

It is a common practice to include both the cat and the butterfly in traditional Chinese paintings. As "cat and butterfly" share the same pronunciation from the term referring to those in their nineties, the painting featuring the cat and butterfly is often gifted to elderly people in the wish that they will live a long life. When working on such paintings, we can also add peony and camellia as a foil to enhance the sense of diversity.

Cat: As the protagonist of the painting, the cat is supposed to be placed in the foreground.

Please refer to Page 148

Butterfly: We can use bright colors to draw the butterfly to make a contrast with the cat.

Please refer to Pages 136 & 137

Peony: The peony is supposed to be positioned in the background.

Please refer to Page 62

Composition: This painting features a simple composition, with the cat and butterfly in the foreground and the peony in the background.

Tiger

Generally speaking, Chinese people will paint tigers in forests or on cliffs. As tigers mostly live in nearly inaccessible forests, the flourishing trees and towering cliffs will help to highlight the valor of the tiger.

Tiger: We can highlight the valor of the tiger. Pay attention to the facial expressions.

Please refer to Page 162

Bush: Draw some bushes to highlight the stoutness of the body.

Please refer to Pages 190 & 191

Composition: The highlight of this painting is positioned in the upper right corner. By placing it at a height, we can successfully capture how intimidating the tiger is.

Rock: Draw the rocks in a way as if they had been chapped or axed.

Travelling on the Donkey

Spring outing, traveling afar or traveling in snow are common subjects in traditional Chinese paintings. The literati tended to mount their horse, donkey or even ox and ride to the countryside to appreciate the beauty of the Nature. When their poetic inspirations were triggered, they would make a poem on the animal's back. Such a casual life was believed to be a defining relaxation for the literati class.

Middle-age Man: The most challenging part about drawing a middle-age man is how to depict his back and a hardly-seen face and how to capture his expressions.

Please refer to Pages 169 & 170

Donkey: Draw the donkey from the side and behind by paying attention to the perspective relationship.

Please refer to Page 155

Composition: The center of gravity is supposed to be placed in the lower left corner, while the upper right corner is meant to exude a sense of spaciousness and distance. In this way, the viewer's eyes will follow the figures in the painting and look from the lower left corner to the upper right corner, indicating the distance.

Lady Leaning on the Balustrades

Lady portraits are a significant genre and a common subject in traditional Chinese paintings. The lady is always placed in courtyards, appreciating the flowers, savoring tea, playing the zither, doing embroidery and relaxing in other ways. In this illustration, a beautiful lady leans on the balustrades and looks into the distance, as if thinking of her lover, or longing for the life outside the residence to which she is confined.

Lady: The lady should look slender and delicate. Pay attention to her eyes.

Please refer to Page 171

Balustrade: Both the balustrade and the pole play a supportive role. We should not spend more efforts on them than on the lady.

Composition: In this painting, the lady is closer to the pole to create dissymmetry. An over-even composition will compromise the attraction of the painting.

Crickets Fight in the Shade of the Chinese Banana Tree

This painting is primarily intended to highlight how cute children are. Two little boys are fighting their crickets under the Chinese banana tree. Aggressive in nature, the crickets have to fight with each other until one of them is down. Generally speaking, children are a favorable subject in traditional Chinese paintings.

Chinese Banana Tree: We could draw two leaves in a simple and suggestive way.

Please refer to Page 60

Little Boy: Both of them have focused their eyes on the box. Pay attention to their facial expressions and gestures.

Please refer to Page 181

Composition: There is a lot to say about the composition. The leaves of the Chinese banana tree in the upper right corner and the figure in the lower left corner have constructed a balance in composition.

TIP

We can employ the same composition to draw little girls engaged in rubber band skipping or imitating family life. ™

Fishing Alone on the River

This painting is intended to illustrate the vastness of the river, and a standard composition featuring a river and two banks is employed. The bush is positioned in the foreground, behind which is a fisherman on the boat. This painting featuring someone fishing alone on the river was a great favorite to ancient Chinese scholars as a symbol of their wish to escape from the mortal world.

Riverbank: The riverbank is an indispensable element in such paintings.

Please refer to Page 207

Bush: The bush is the protagonist in the foreground.

Please refer to Page 199

Boat: A boat can be finished in several simple strokes. There is no need to work on the details of the boat which is intended as an adornment.

Please refer to Pages 190 & 191

Composition: This composition featuring a river and two banks comes from Ni Zan, a renowned Yuan painter. Ni Zan is good at capturing the sense of vastness and desolation to express his wish to escape from the mortal world and solely focus on a simplistic lifestyle. This typical Ni Zan style was a valued heritage for landscape painters in the dynasties to come.

Deep Mountains

This painting is intended to illustrate the towering mountains. The picture is quite occupied to highlight the imposingness of the mountains. In the foreground are the bush and trees. Against the stream, falls and the path, an ancient temple is hidden in the deep mountains, and only the roof and the inscription banners are visible. In traditional Chinese paintings, a suggestive approach is valued. In this painting, only a part of the ancient temple is revealed. Obscured by the flourishing trees and giant rocks the ancient temple looks more mysterious.

Hill: The key is to capture the imposing properties the hill projects.

Please refer to Page 209

Path: The path is a small but interesting element in landscape paintings.

Bush: The bush is usually applied in the foreground in landscape paintings.

Please refer to Pages 190 & 191

Falls: The narrow ravines can always help to highlight how towering the hill is.

Please refer to Page 213

Ancient Temple: Only a certain part needs to be included in the painting, such as the roof and the inscription banner.

Composition: The picture looks relatively occupied, with only small parts unpainted. Such a composition is optimal to represent the towering mountains in North China.

Farming Life

Farming life is a common subject in traditional Chinese paintings. A farmhouse, a small field, an ox, several chicks and ducks, sowing in the spring and harvesting in the autumn, a totally self-sufficient life is the most comfortable for ancient Chinese. In this painting, we will incorporate the farmhouse, bridge, pagoda tree and the fence which we talk about in the former chapters. An interesting painting featuring the farming life is thus finished.

Farmhouse: It is the center of the painting. It is necessary to work on the details.

Please refer to Pages 200 & 201

Pine: The pine behind the farmhouse and some unnamed trees are placed in the point of height.

Please refer to Page 92

Fence & Bridge: The bridge and fence play a secondary role in the painting.

Please refer to Pages 194, 195, 196 & 197

Composition: This painting exemplifies a flat-and-horizontal composition. The only high spot in the painting is the farmhouse as well as the tree behind the farmhouse. Such a composition works best to illustrate the plains in North China.

Author: Zheng Zhonghua

Project Editors: Guo Guang, Mang Yu, Chen Jingsha

English Editors: Fiona Wang, Dora Ding

English Translator: Coral Yee

Copy Editor: Lee Perkins

Book Designers: Zhang Yuhai, Zhang Xuxing

Guide to Chinese Brush Painting

First published in the United Kingdom in 2011 by CYPI PRESS

Add: 79 College Road, Harrow Middlesex, HA1 1BD, UK
E-mail: sales@cypi.net   editor@cypi.net
Website: www.cypi.co.uk
ISBN: 978-1-908175-10-6
Printed in China